Glencoe

EARTH SCIENCE

STUDY GUIDE
Teacher Edition

GLENCOE
McGraw-Hill

New York, New York   Columbus, Ohio   Mission Hills, California   Peoria, Illinois

A GLENCOE PROGRAM
Glencoe Earth Science

Student Edition
Teacher Wraparound Edition
Study Guide, SE and TE
Reinforcement, SE and TE
Enrichment, SE and TE
Concept Mapping
Critical Thinking/Problem Solving
Activity Worksheets
Chapter Review
Chapter Review Software
Laboratory Manual, SE and TE

Transparency Packages:
  Teaching Transparencies
  Section Focus Transparencies
  Science Integration Transparencies

The Glencoe Science Professional Development Series:
  Performance Assessment in the Science Classroom
  Lab and Safety Skills in the Science Classroom
  Cooperative Learning in the Science Classroom
  Alternate Assessment in the Science Classroom
  Exploring Environmental Issues

Science Integration Activities
Cross-Curricular Integration
Science and Society Integration
Technology Integration
Multicultural Connections
Performance Assessment
Assessment—Chapter and Unit Tests
Spanish Resources
MindJogger Videoquizzes and Teacher Guide
English/Spanish Audiocassettes
CD–ROM Multimedia System
Interactive Videodisc Program
Computer Test Bank—DOS and Macintosh

TO THE TEACHER

Each chapter of *Glencoe Earth Science* is divided into three to five numbered sections or lessons. The Study Guide worksheet provides the average to below average student with an aid to learning and understanding the vocabulary and major concepts in each numbered section of the chapter. You may want to have students work on the Study Guide as you make a reading assignment for a particular section. Reduced answer pages appear at the end of the booklet.

Glencoe/McGraw-Hill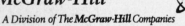
A Division of The McGraw-Hill Companies

Send all inquiries to:
Glencoe/McGraw-Hill
936 Eastwind Drive
Westerville, OH 43081

Printed in the United States of America

ISBN 0-02-827193-9

1 2 3 4 5 6 7 8 9 10 MAL 04 03 02 01 00 99 98 97 96

TABLE OF CONTENTS

Chapter 1

STUDY GUIDE

• What Is Earth Science?

Use the terms in the box to complete the sentences.

science	physics	astronomy
chemistry	Earth science	meteorology
life science	geology	oceanography

_____ **1.** _____ is a process of observing and studying things in our world.

_____ **2.** The four major sciences include _____ , life science, chemistry, and physics.

_____ **3.** _____ is the science that studies living organisms.

_____ **4.** The science of _____ is the study of objects in space.

_____ **5.** When you study forces, motion, energy, and their effects on matter, you are studying _____ .

_____ **6.** In _____ , scientists study Earth, its matter, and the processes that form and change Earth.

_____ **7.** _____ is the study of the properties and composition of matter.

_____ **8.** The study of weather and the forces and processes that cause it is called _____ .

_____ **9.** In _____ , people study the processes that occur within the ocean and the effects humans have on these processes.

Complete Items 10 and 11 on the lines provided.

10. List four specific areas of study of Earth science.

_____

_____

_____

_____

11. Use Table 1-1 in your text. What will you study in Earth science? _____

_____

_____

Chapter 1

STUDY GUIDE

● Applying Science

Unscramble the scrambled words. Put your answers in the blanks provided to complete the paragraph. Then answer the questions.

Technology is the use of **enifitsicc** _____ discoveries. Technology has enabled

people to clear **sterofs** _____ and build cities. It's led to the development of

modern **camshine** _____ such as cars and computers. Because of technology,

work that is dangerous for people to do can now be done by **stoobr** _____ .

People can now live longer because **cloghoteny** _____ has improved medicines,

health care, and foods. Technology is responsible for many improvements, but it has also created

brompels _____ . Some uses of technology cause **loptulnoi** _____ .

For example, air conditioners can keep rooms cool, but they also release a chemical that can harm the

montinvener _____ .

1. What is the topic of the paragraph? _____

2. What is technology? _____
   _____

3. Name the machines identified in the paragraph. _____
   _____

4. Why are robots useful to people? _____
   _____

5. How has technology helped people live longer? _____
   _____
   _____

6. Does technology cause any problems? Explain. _____
   _____

7. How are air conditioners helpful to people? _____
   _____

8. How can air conditioners be harmful? _____
   _____

● Solving Problems

In the blank, write the letter of the term or phrase that best completes each statement.

_____ 1. The first step in any problem-solving strategy is to _____ .
   a. collect information about the problem   **b.** identify the problem

_____ 2. The method used by scientists for solving problems is known as the _____ .
   a. control   **b.** scientific method

_____ 3. A prediction about a problem that can be tested is a _____ .
   a. hypothesis   **b.** conclusion

_____ 4. A _____ is a standard for comparison in an experiment.
   a. variable   **b.** control

_____ 5. An explanation backed by results obtained from repeated tests or experiments is a _____ .
   a. theory   **b.** variable

_____ 6. A process that uses certain skills to solve problems is called _____ .
   a. theory   **b.** critical thinking

_____ 7. A _____ is a changeable factor in an experiment.
   a. variable   **b.** control

_____ 8. The best experiments test only one _____ at a time.
   a. variable   **b.** control

_____ 9. If a conclusion does not support a hypothesis, the _____ .
   a. experiment did not work properly   **b.** hypothesis should be revised

_____ 10. If a hypothesis is supported by new data gathered over a period of time, it may become a _____ .
   a. control   **b.** theory

_____ 11. Making lists, drawing graphs, making a model, and eliminating possibilities are all _____ for solving problems.
   a. strategies   **b.** variables

_____ 12. If a hypothesis has been backed by results from repeated tests or experiments, it becomes a _____ .
   a. variable   **b.** theory

Chapter 1
STUDY GUIDE

• Measurement and Safety

Find the words or prefixes in the puzzle that match the definitions below. Circle the words in the puzzle. Then write each word next to its definition.

```
W  E  I  G  H  T  G  S
C  V  A  R  E  A  R  K
E  O  M  A  S  S  A  E
N  L  G  R  A  M  V  L
T  U  M  I  L  L  I  V
I  M  E  T  E  R  T  I
D  E  N  S  I  T  Y  N
I  C  E  L  S  I  U  S
```

_____ 1. Measure of the amount of matter in an object

_____ 2. Temperature measurement in which freezing is 0° and boiling is 100°

_____ 3. Amount of surface within a set of boundaries

_____ 4. Prefix meaning one hundredth

_____ 5. Force that pulls particles of matter toward other particles of matter

_____ 6. Standard unit in SI of length

_____ 7. Measure of the amount of matter that occupies a space

_____ 8. Standard unit in SI for temperature

_____ 9. Measure of the force of gravity that is expressed in newtons

_____ 10. Standard unit in SI of measure for mass

_____ 11. Measure of how much space an object occupies

_____ 12. Prefix meaning one thousandth

_____ 13. What two letters were not circled in the puzzle?

Answer the questions on the lines provided.

14. What are the two letters SI an abbreviation for? _____

15. Why must safe practices and methods be used in laboratory activities? _____

_____

Chapter 2

STUDY GUIDE

● Atoms

Circle the term in parentheses that makes each statement correct.

1. Protons are particles (outside, in) the nucleus of an atom.

2. Electrons are atomic particles with a (positive, negative) charge.

3. An example of matter is (air, heat).

4. The building blocks of matter are (atoms, compounds).

5. (Neutrons, Protons) are particles in the atom's nucleus that have no electric charge.

6. The atomic particles outside of the atom's nucleus are (electrons, protons).

7. Substances made up of only one kind of atom are called (isotopes, elements).

8. Isotopes are atoms of the same element that have different numbers of (neutrons, protons).

9. Negatively charged particles that move around the atom's nucleus are (neutrons, electrons).

10. Two atoms of the same element that have different (mass numbers, atomic numbers) are

    isotopes of the element.

11. A difference in the (mass number, atomic number) of atoms means the atoms are of different

    elements.

12. The nucleus of an atom has a (positive, negative) charge.

13. Carbon-14 is an (isotope, element) of carbon.

14. The mass number of an atom with 12 protons and 12 neutrons is (12, 24).

15. The atomic number of an atom is equal to the number of (protons, neutrons) in its nucleus.

16. In atoms with equal numbers of electrons and protons, there is (a positive, no) electric charge.

17. Anything that takes up space and has mass is (matter, an element).

18. A model of an atom is (larger, smaller) than the actual atom.

19. The nucleus of an atom is made up of neutrons and (electrons, protons).

20. Isotopes enable scientists to determine the (age, size) of ancient objects.

Chapter 2

Text Pages 38–43

STUDY GUIDE

● Combinations of Atoms

Use the words in the box to complete the statements. You will use the words more than once.

molecule	compound	chemical properties	ions	mixture

1. The components of a _____ can be separated by physical means.

2. The _____ of an element determine how the element will change when it reacts with another element.

3. A _____ is a substance that has different properties from the elements in it.

4. Combined atoms form a _____ .

5. Electrically charged atoms are _____ .

6. Table salt is an example of a _____ .

7. An example of a _____ is salt water.

8. Table salt is formed when the _____ of sodium and chlorine combine.

9. Iron rusts when it comes in contact with water because of its _____ .

10. The atoms of hydrogen and oxygen combine to form a _____ of the compound water.

Identify the two atoms that are ions. Label the negatively charged ion with a minus sign. Label the positively charged ion with a plus sign.

11 protons	8 protons	17 protons
12 neutrons	8 neutrons	18 neutrons
10 electrons	8 electrons	18 electrons
_____	_____	_____

Chapter 2
STUDY GUIDE

● Matter

Change the italicized word in each statement to make the statement correct.

1. The *size* of an object determines whether it will float in water. _____
_____

2. Orange juice and milk are both *solids*. _____
_____

3. Stars are made up of matter in the *gaseous* state. _____
_____

4. An object's density is equal to its mass divided by its *length*. _____
_____

5. Matter with atoms in a fixed position in relation to one another is in the *liquid* state. _____
_____
_____

6. Density and state of matter are *chemical* properties. _____
_____

7. *Hydrogen* is the only substance that occurs naturally on Earth as a gas, a liquid, and a solid.
_____
_____

8. The *physical* properties of a liquid do not change when it becomes a gas. _____
_____

9. *Liquids* fill their entire container regardless of the container's size or shape. _____
_____
_____

10. On Earth the *solid* state of matter is least common. _____
_____

Chapter 2

STUDY GUIDE

Text Pages 54–59

● Energy from Atoms

Match each description in Column I with the correct term in Column II. Write the letter of the correct term in the blank at the left.

Column I

_____ 1. Location of ore deposits used to make fuel for nuclear reactors

_____ 2. Long metal pipes that sit in water in a nuclear reactor

_____ 3. The splitting of the nuclei of heavy elements

_____ 4. Site of a proposed nuclear waste storage facility

_____ 5. Source of most of the electricity generated by power plants in the United States

_____ 6. Source of rock used to make fuel for nuclear power plants

_____ 7. Most commonly used fuel in fission power plants

_____ 8. Highly radioactive material produced by nuclear power plants

_____ 9. Particles that begin a heat-releasing chain reaction when fired into fuel rods in a nuclear reactor

_____ 10. Energy source produced from nuclear reactions

Column II

a. fission

b. Rocky Mountains

c. neutrons

d. fuel rods

e. uranium-235 isotope

f. Yucca Mountain

g. nuclear waste

h. sandstone

i. nuclear energy

j. fossil fuels

Answer the following questions on the lines provided.

11. What are three major hazards for possible nuclear waste storage sites? _____

_____

_____

12. How is heat released during an atomic reaction used to produce electricity in a nuclear reactor?

_____

_____

13. Why do some people oppose plans by the U.S. Department of Energy to construct a nuclear waste

storage facility in Nevada? _____

_____

_____

Chapter 3
STUDY GUIDE

• Minerals

Find the error in each statement. Rewrite the statement correctly on the line provided.

1. A mineral is a solid that comes from organic matter. _____

_____

2. Salt, diamonds, graphite, and coal are minerals. _____

_____

3. The compounds in a mineral are arranged in a repeating pattern to form crystals. _____

_____

4. Some minerals form from magma, which is hot, liquid rock material on Earth's surface. _____

_____

_____

5. Halite crystals are formed when fresh lake water evaporates. _____

_____

6. The smallest group of rock-forming minerals consists of silicates. _____

_____

In the blank at the left, write the term in the box that correctly completes each statement.

crystal	halide	silicates	4000	8
carbonates	elements	oxides	98 percent	6

_____ 7. Scientists know of more than _____ minerals.

_____ 8. Most of these are composed of only _____ elements.

_____ 9. These few elements make up _____ of Earth's crust.

_____ 10. Minerals that combine to form the most common rock-forming group are _____ .

_____ 11. A group that includes rock salt is the _____ group.

_____ 12. Each mineral has a different _____ formation.

_____ 13. Scientists have identified _____ major formation systems.

_____ 14. Two other major groups of minerals are _____ and _____ .

Chapter 3

STUDY GUIDE

• Mineral Identification

Match the terms in Column I with the phrases in Column II. Write the letter of the correct phrase in the blank on the left.

Column I

_____ 1. cleavage

_____ 2. diamond

_____ 3. fracture

_____ 4. hardness

_____ 5. mica

_____ 6. luster

_____ 7. Mohs

_____ 8. quartz

_____ 9. streak

_____ 10. talc

Column II

a. The measure of how easily a mineral can be scratched

b. Name given to the scale of hardness

c. One of the softest known minerals

d. The hardest known mineral

e. Reflection of light from a mineral's surface

f. Color left by powdered mineral on unglazed porcelain

g. Tendency to break along smooth, flat surfaces

h. A common mineral that breaks along smooth, flat surfaces

i. Tendency to break with rough or jagged edges

j. A common mineral that breaks with rough or jagged edges

Answer the following question on the lines provided.

11. What three tests would you perform to help you identify an unknown mineral?

_____

_____

_____

_____

_____

_____

In the blanks at the left, write the terms that correctly complete each statement.

_____ **12.** The mineral _____ is sometimes confused with gold because both minerals are the color of _____.

_____ **13.** The mineral _____ is soft enough to leave a streak on paper and is commonly used in _____.

Chapter 3
STUDY GUIDE

• Uses of Minerals

Use the words in the box to fill in the blanks. Some words may be used more than once.

aluminum	amethyst	crystal	demand
expense	gems	ores	polished
profit	rare	supply	
traces	useful	value	

Stones called _____ are highly prized minerals because they are beautiful

and often _____ . Many gemstones have a _____

structure that allows them to be cut and _____ to the high quality needed for

jewelry. The difference between a gemstone and the common form of the same mineral is sometimes

slight. The purple stone _____ , for example, is quartz with just

_____ of iron in its structure.

Some minerals contain a _____ substance that can be mined at a

_____ . Such minerals are called _____ . Bauxite is

this kind of mineral because _____ can be taken from it and made into

_____ products. In most cases, waste rock or material must be removed

before a mineral can be used. If the _____ of mining gets higher than the

_____ of the material, the mineral is no longer considered to be an ore. The

value of the material can also change if the _____ or the demand increases

or decreases.

Use words in the box at the top of the page that fit to complete the puzzle.

```
        ____ ____  M  ____
     ____ ____ ____  I  ____
  ____ ____ ____ ____  N  ____
     ____ ____  E  ____ ____ ____ ____ ____
        ____ ____  R  ____ ____
        ____ ____  A  ____ ____ ____
  ____ ____ ____ ____ ____ ____  L
```

Chapter 3

STUDY GUIDE

● Uses of Titanium

In the puzzle below, find and circle eight examples of things that can be made of titanium.

1.

```
V  W  E  M  O  S  P  R  I  N  G  A
A  B  H  I  S  M  I  Q  U  O  A  R
L  I  K  E  R  E  S  N  R  Y  S  T
V  K  R  S  E  E  R  O  A  B  O  I
E  L  D  P  N  L  I  L  V  W  T  F
D  A  G  O  L  F  C  L  U  B  E  I
S  B  S  O  E  A  W  H  I  V  K  C
Q  U  T  C  O  S  N  K  A  J  C  I
S  B  I  C  Y  C  L  E  R  I  A  A
A  L  C  I  B  B  Y  L  A  N  R  L
T  A  T  M  M  H  O  L  S  P  R  H
S  P  R  I  N  E  T  L  L  Y  O  I
W  O  L  L  E  P  H  B  V  W  S  P
```

Answer the following questions on the lines provided.

2. Why are many artificial body parts made of titanium? _____

_____

3. Why are manufacturers more likely to obtain titanium from rutile than from ilmenite?

_____

_____

_____

Chapter 4

STUDY GUIDE

Text Pages 86–96

● The Rock Cycle

Match the items in Column I with the terms in Column II. Write the letter of the correct term in the blank at the left.

Column I

_____ 1. A naturally occurring, nonliving solid with a definite structure and composition

_____ 2. A mixture of minerals, mineraloids, glass, or organic matter

_____ 3. Processes by which rocks form and change

_____ 4. A hard silicate mineral

_____ 5. An igneous rock made up of mica, feldspar, quartz, and hornblende

Column II

a. rock

b. mineral

c. quartz

d. granite

e. rock cycle

In the blank, write the term that correctly completes each sentence. Use the information in the textbook.

6. If the minerals in a sedimentary rock melt and then cool, they can form a(n) _____ rock.

7. Quartz is a common _____ found in rocks.

8. Sedimentary and igneous rocks can be changed into metamorphic rocks by _____ and _____ .

9. If an igneous rock weathers and erodes into fragments, the fragments can form a(n) _____ rock.

10. Weathering and erosion are two of the _____ that change rocks.

Write each word in the box under the correct heading.

weathering	igneous	melting	cooling
erosion	sedimentary	compaction	cementation
deposition	heating	metamorphic	

Processes in the rock cycle

_____   _____

_____   _____

_____   _____

_____   _____

Kinds of rocks

_____

_____

_____

Chapter 4

STUDY GUIDE

• Igneous Rocks

Use the words in the box to fill in the blanks

200	iron	slow	lava
fine	1400	lighter	dense
magma	large	silicon	abundant
formation	surface	igneous	granitic
basaltic	radioactive	crystals	pressure
intrusive	extrusive	minerals	magnification

Most _____ originates 60 to _____ below

Earth's surface. Temperatures reach about _____ °C at these depths.

In certain locations, _____ and heat caused by overlying rocks and

_____ elements produce magma. Rocks formed from molten Earth materials

are _____ rocks. When magma cools below Earth's surface, it forms

_____ -grained, _____ igneous rocks. The

_____ of these common rocks grow large because of the

_____ rate of cooling. When magma moves to Earth's

_____ , it is called _____ . When lava cools on

Earth's surface, it forms _____ -grained, _____

igneous rocks. Minerals of extrusive rocks are so small that _____ is needed

for identification. Igneous rocks can be classified by their _____ . They can

also be classified by the types of _____ in them.

_____ igneous rocks are dark-colored, heavy, and _____ .

They contain _____ and magnesium. _____

igneous rocks are _____ -colored and less dense. They contain a lot of oxygen

and _____ . Igneous rocks are the most _____

on Earth.

Chapter 4
STUDY GUIDE

• Metamorphic Rocks

Determine whether each of the following statements is true or false. Write the word "true" or "false" in the blank. If the sentence is false, rewrite it so that it is true.

_____ **1.** Metamorphic rocks are rocks that have been changed by temperature and pressure.

_____

_____ **2.** Nonfoliated rock will separate easily into layers.

_____

_____ **3.** Pressure does not play a role in the formation of metamorphic rocks.

_____

_____ **4.** A metamorphic rock with a foliated texture has bands of minerals.

_____

_____ **5.** Metamorphic rocks can be formed from changes in igneous, sedimentary, or other metamorphic rocks.

_____

_____ **6.** Sandstone is a metamorphic rock.

_____

_____ **7.** A metamorphic rock with no banding is nonfoliated.

_____

_____ **8.** The mineral grains in metamorphic rocks may be flattened.

_____

Complete the chart using information in your textbook.

Type of rock	Can change into	Metamorphic rock
Sedimentary		
Shale	⟶	_____
Sandstone	⟶	_____
Igneous		
Basalt	⟶	_____
Granite	⟶	_____
Metamorphic		
Slate	⟶	_____

Chapter 4

STUDY GUIDE

Text Pages 101–107

• Sedimentary Rocks

Answer the following questions on the lines provided.

1. What are sediments? _____

   _____

   _____

2. What are sedimentary rocks? _____

   _____

3. What is compaction? _____

   _____

   _____

4. What is cementation? _____

   _____

5. What are detrital sedimentary rocks? _____

   _____

6. What is conglomerate? _____

   _____

7. What is breccia? _____

   _____

8. What are chemical sedimentary rocks? _____

9. What are organic sedimentary rocks? _____

   _____

10. What is coquina? _____

    _____

11. What is chalk? _____

    _____

Chapter 4

STUDY GUIDE

• Burning Waste Coal

Answer the following questions on the lines provided.

1. How does the process of cogeneration differ from other processes for generating power?

_____

_____

2. What problems are caused by the piles of waste coal found near abandoned coal mines?

_____

_____

Put an X by each statement that does not agree with your textbook.

_____ 3. Coal is an organic sedimentary rock.

_____ 4. Coal no longer provides fuel for electricity in the United States.

_____ 5. Waste coal is the result of new mining techniques.

_____ 6. Acid runoff results when rain flows through piles of waste coal.

_____ 7. Mixing waste coal with limestone before burning removes more than 90 percent of harmful sulfur dioxide emissions.

_____ 8. The ash that results from burning waste coal changes to a low-grade cement when it mixes with water.

_____ 9. Some companies use waste coal to generate electrical energy, but the thermal energy that is generated cannot be used.

_____ 10. Waste coal is what remains after coal is burned.

Chapter 5

STUDY GUIDE

• Landforms

Answer the following questions on the lines provided.

1. What are the three basic types of landforms? _____

2. What are the four types of mountains? _____

Match each description in Column I with the correct term in Column II. Write the letter of the correct term in the blank at the left.

Column I

_____ **3.** Large, relatively flat areas of land

_____ **4.** Large areas of horizontal rocks that have been uplifted and that rise steeply above the land around the rocks

_____ **5.** Distance above or below sea level

_____ **6.** Grassy wetlands usually flooded with water

_____ **7.** Broad, flat lowlands along coastlines

_____ **8.** Land features that rise high above the surrounding land

_____ **9.** Type of mountains formed when rock layers are squeezed from opposite sides

_____ **10.** Type of mountains formed when crust was pushed up by forces inside Earth

_____ **11.** Type of mountains formed when huge tilted blocks of rocks are separated from surrounding rock by faults

_____ **12.** Type of mountains formed when molten material reaches Earth's surface through a weak area in the crust

Column II

a. folded mountains

b. plains

c. marshes

d. fault-block mountains

e. elevation

f. plateaus

g. volcanic mountains

h. mountains

i. coastal plains

j. upwarped mountains

Chapter 5

STUDY GUIDE

• Viewpoints

Match the descriptions in Column I with the terms in Column II. Write the letter of the correct term in the blank on the left.

Column I

_____ 1. An imaginary line that circles Earth exactly halfway between the North and South poles

_____ 2. A reference point for east/west grid lines that runs through Greenwich, England, from the North Pole to the South Pole

_____ 3. A line at the 180 degree meridian

_____ 4. Lines that run north and south and determine locations east or west of the prime meridian

_____ 5. Lines that run parallel to the equator and determine north and south locations

Column II

a. latitude

b. longitude

c. equator

d. prime meridian

e. International Date Line

Use the words in the box to fill in the blanks.

15	24	spinning	lost
one	nighttime	gained	longitude

When it is daytime for half of Earth, it is _____ for the other half.

Time is always changing because Earth is constantly _____. Earth is divided

into _____ time zones. Each division is _____

degrees wide and has a _____ -hour difference in time from the previous

15° meridian. A meridian is a line of _____ . At the International Date Line,

one day is _____ going west, and one day is _____

going east across the line.

Chapter 5

STUDY GUIDE

• Maps

Use the worlds in the box to fill in the blanks.

models	small areas	distorted	larger
legend	projection	Robinson projection	contour
Mercator projection	globe	topographic	scale
flat	curved	contour interval	conic projection

Maps are _____ of Earth's surface. The best model, because of

Earth's shape, would be a _____ . A convenient paper model of Earth,

however, would be a map projection. On a map _____ , the points and lines

of Earth's _____ surface are transferred onto a _____

piece of paper. A _____ shows all lines of latitude and all lines of

longitude as parallel lines. This projection distorts areas near the poles, showing them

_____ than they actually are. On a _____ ,

lines of latitude are parallel and lines of longitude are curved. Landmasses near the poles

are not _____ on this type of map projection. By projecting points and lines

from a globe onto a cone, a _____ may be drawn. This projection

is used to make accurate maps of _____ .

A _____ map shows the changes in elevation of Earth's surface. This

map shows _____ lines which connect points on Earth's surface of equal

elevation. The lines are drawn at specific intervals. The distance between the contour lines is the

_____ . A map _____ gives the relationship

between the distances on the map and the actual distances on Earth's surface. The map

_____ explains what the symbols used on the topographic map mean.

Chapter 5

STUDY GUIDE

• Mapping Our Planet

Use the words in the box to complete the statements.

radar	Sea Beam	distance
ocean	calculated	dozen
sound	speed	gravitational force
receiving	Landsat	colors
Topex-Poseidon	echo	time

1. A _____ Satellite uses a mirror to detect wavelengths of energy reflected from Earth's surface.

2. The _____ Satellite computes the distance between the satellite and the ocean's surface.

3. The high-frequency radio waves that are transmitted by the Topex-Poseidon Satellite are also known as _____ waves.

4. Information gathered from Landsat satellites is used to show different wavelengths of energy as _____ .

5. Ocean water forms bulges over mountains and depressions over valleys because there is more _____ between ocean water and large structures on the ocean floor.

6. _____ is a new sonar technology.

7. Sonar refers to the use of _____ waves to detect structures on the _____ bottom.

8. Sea Beam sends a _____ wave from the bottom of the ship toward the _____ floor.

9. The sound wave bounces off the ocean floor and an _____ of the sound wave is picked up by a _____ device.

10. The _____ the sound wave traveled is _____ by a computer.

11. The computer uses the _____ of the sound in the water and the _____ it takes for the sound to be reflected to make the calculations.

12. An equipped Sea Beam has more than a _____ sonar devices.

Chapter 6

Text Pages 148–155

STUDY GUIDE

● Weathering

Use the words to fill in the blanks of the paragraphs.

plants	pieces	moisture	ice wedging	acids	carbonic acid
freezing	chemical	oxidation	temperatures	minerals	
climate	desert	mechanical	cracks	reacting	

Weathering is the breaking of rocks into _____ . There are two main types

of weathering. _____ weathering involves breaking rocks without changing

their chemical composition. In _____ , water trapped in rocks freezes and

expands, forcing the rocks apart. _____ can also cause mechanical weathering.

As their roots grow and put pressure on rocks, _____ widen and rock

fragments may fall off. _____ weathering involves water, air, and other

substances' _____ with the minerals in the rocks. When metal is

exposed to water and oxygen, _____ occurs and rust forms.

_____ in plant roots and mosses can also react with the

_____ in rocks. Water and carbon dioxide combine to form

_____ , which reacts with minerals such as calcite in limestone. How rapidly

weathering occurs in an area depends on the _____ . Chemical weathering

happens more slowly in _____ areas due to a lack of

_____ . Low _____ in polar regions keep chemical

weathering to a minimum there. Whenever _____ and thawing alternate,

mechanical weathering becomes an important form of weathering.

Chapter 6

STUDY GUIDE

• Soil

Use the terms in the box to complete the sentences. Use the information in your textbook.

soil	humus	*A* horizon
horizons	composition	below
topsoil	parent	top
evolve	bottom	leaching
soil profile	water	

1. _____ is a mixture of sediments of weathered rock and organic matter.

2. Decaying plant and animal matter is called _____ .

3. Due to weathering, different layers, or _____ , of soil form.

4. Soil generally has three layers, and these make up a _____.

5. The *A* horizon is the _____ layer and is also known as

   _____ .

6. The *B* horizon is the layer _____ the *A* horizon.

7. The *C* horizon is the _____ layer in a soil profile; it contains partly

   weathered rock but no humus.

8. Below the bottom horizon is _____ rock.

9. You can tell that the _____ is the most fully evolved soil layer because it

   has more humus and smaller rock fragments than the other layers.

10. _____ moving downward through the horizons dissolves and carries

    minerals into lower horizons by the process of _____ .

11. The thickness of the soil layers and their _____ depend on the climate, slope

    of the land, and the type of rock in an area and how long the soil has been evolving.

12. Soil horizons _____ more slowly in an area that has little rainfall

    because chemical weathering occurs slowly in a dry climate.

Chapter 6

STUDY GUIDE

● Land Use and Soil Loss

Match the items in Column I with the terms in Column II. Write the letter of the correct term in the blank at the left.

Column I

_____ 1. Practice of leaving plant stalks in the field

_____ 2. Mechanical turning and loosening of the soil

_____ 3. Trees and plants in tropical regions

_____ 4. Desert formation

_____ 5. Practice of alternating crops that cover the ground with crops that leave the land exposed

Column II

a. plowing

b. rain forest

c. strip cropping

d. desertification

e. no-till farming

Decide whether each of the following statements is true or false. Write the word "true" or "false" in the blank. If the statement is false, rewrite it so that it is true.

_____ 6. Soil loss is particularly severe in the tropics.

_____

_____

_____ 7. Plants are important to soil, because without them, soil evolution stops and no new soil develops. _____

_____

_____

_____ 8. Desertification is a slow process that affects very little land each year.

_____

_____

_____

_____ 9. In dry areas, farmers minimize soil erosion by plowing under the natural vegetation. _____

_____

_____

_____ 10. Soil can easily recover the nutrients that crops use up.

_____

_____

_____

Chapter 7

STUDY GUIDE

● **Gravity**

Solve the following crossword puzzle by using the clues provided.

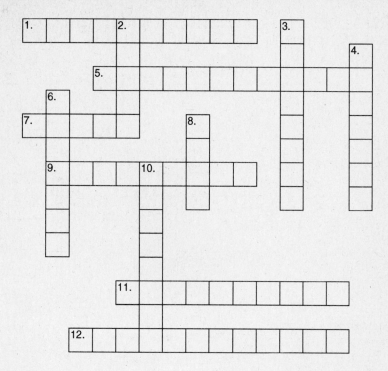

Across

1. The dropping of sediment

5. An agent of erosion

7. Sediments slowly moving downhill, especially after freezing and thawing

9. Bits and pieces of rocks, soil, insects, and animals that have been transported

11. Large rocks breaking loose and falling quickly to the bottom

12. Large amounts of sediments sliding downhill

Down

2. Loose materials or rock layers slipping downward as one large mass

3. An agent of erosion

4. An agent of erosion

6. Process that wears away sediments and transports them from one location to another

8. An agent of erosion

10. Masses of a thick, pasty substance made of water and sediment that slide downhill

Use the words in the box to fill in the blanks.

| energy of motion | rockslides | mudflows | gravity |

13. _____ happen most often during earthquakes.

14. Agents of erosion carry sediment only when they have _____ .

15. _____ often occur in fairly dry areas.

16. Mudflows, creep, slump, and rockslides all depend on _____ to make them happen.

Chapter 7
STUDY GUIDE

Text Pages 178–179

• Developing Land Prone to Erosion

Use the code given to decode the message. Note that in the code, one letter simply stands for another. Write your answer in the spaces provided, placing one letter on each space. The first word of the message is decoded for you.

A B C D E F G H I J K L M N O P Q R S T U V W X Y Z
Code: B C D E F G H I J K L M N O P Q R S T U V W X Y Z A

PEOPLE _____
QFPQMF DBO IFMQ SFEVDF FSPTJPO

_____
JO NBOZ XBZT. UIFZ DBO QMBOU

_____
WFHFUBUJPO. QMBGOU SPPUT IPME

_____
TPJM BOE QMBOUT BCTPSC MPUT PG

_____
XBUFS. QFPQMF XIP MJWF PO

_____
TMPQFT DBO CVJME UFSSBDFT.

_____
UFSSBDFT DBO TMPX UIF FOFSHZ

_____
PG NPUJPO PG XBUFS. QFPQMF PO

_____
TMPQFT BOE OFBS TUSFBNT, MBLFT,

_____
BOE PDFBOT DBO CVJME SFUBJOJOH

_____
XBMMT. UIFZ DBO LFFQ TPJM BOE

_____
SPDLT GSPN TMJEJOH EPXOIJMM.

• Glaciers

Determine whether each of the following statements is true or false. Write the word "true" or "false" in the blank. If the statement is false, change the italicized term to make the statement true.

_____ 1. The glaciers in Greenland and Antarctica are *continental* glaciers.

_____

_____ 2. The usually long, parallel scars gouged into bedrock by glaciers are known as *cirques*. _____

_____ 3. Valleys eroded by glaciers are usually *V-shaped*.

_____

_____ 4. *Till* is the sediments that drop from the base of a glacier as it stops moving. _____

_____ 5. Moraines are mounds of material formed by deposits of glacial *outwash*. _____

_____ 6. Meltwater forms a winding ridge of sand and gravel known as an *esker*. _____

_____ 7. Glacial *plucking* can create a cirque, or bowl-shaped basin, on a mountainside. _____

_____ 8. One type of *till* deposits is an alluvial fan of glacially eroded sediments.

_____

_____ 9. *Icebergs* are sources of fresh water. _____

_____ 10. *Plucking* is the process by which rocks and soil are added to the sides and bottom of a glacier when water freezes and melts.

_____

_____ 11. Very large striations are called glacial *cracks*.

_____

_____ 12. The two types of glacial *deposits* are till and outwash.

_____

_____ 13. Scientists have been studying ways to tow *valley glaciers*.

_____

_____ 14. The Great Lakes were gouged out by *glacial ice*.

_____

Chapter 7

STUDY GUIDE

● Wind

The important ideas in a textbook chapter often are easier to understand if you organize them into a chart. The chart can also help you better remember the information. The chart that follows is on erosion and deposition by the wind. It is only partially filled in. Use the headings and the information provided in Chapter 7 to complete the chart.

Wind erosion

Type: deflation
Description:
Type: abrasion
Description:

Deposition by the wind

Type: loess
Description:
Type: dunes
Description:

Use the types of wind erosion and deposition to complete these statements.

1. Wind erosion similar to sandblasting is _____

2. Some midwestern farmland in the United States is covered by _____ .

3. The most common wind deposits are _____ .

4. In _____ , wind picks up and moves small sediments but leaves heavier pebbles and rocks behind.

5. Tightly packed wind deposits of fine particles are called _____ .

6. Sand _____ are constantly changing and moving as the wind erodes them.

7. _____ causes the pitting and polishing of rocks and sediments.

8. Both abrasion and _____ are common in areas where there are few plants to protect sediments.

STUDY GUIDE

● Surface Water

In the blank at the left, write the letter of the term or phrase that correctly completes each statement.

_____ 1. Water runoff forms small _____ .
    a. water cycles   **b.** drainage   **c.** streams   **d.** overflows

_____ 2. The land area from which a stream gets its water is its _____ .
    a. overflow   **b.** drainage basin   **c.** runoff   **d.** river system

_____ 3. The largest drainage basin in the United States is that of the _____ .
    a. Missouri River   **c.** Appalachian Mountains
    b. Rocky Mountains   **d.** Mississippi River

_____ 4. Most of the rain that falls between the Rocky Mountains and the Appalachian Mountains flows into the _____ .
    a. Missouri and Ohio rivers   **c.** Rocky Mountains
    b. Appalachian Mountains   **d.** Pacific Ocean

_____ 5. A stream that flows swiftly through a steep valley is a _____ stream.
    a. mature   **b.** shallow   **c.** old   **d.** young

_____ 6. The broad, flat valley floor cut by a stream is a _____ .
    a. floodplain   **b.** meander   **c.** drainage system   **d.** mature river

_____ 7. A curve in the river formed by erosion is called a _____ .
    a. floodplain   **b.** meander   **c.** drainage system   **d.** mature river

The diagrams show young, mature, or old rivers. Label each diagram correctly.

8. _____   9. _____   10. _____

Chapter 8

STUDY GUIDE

• Groundwater

In the blank at the left, write a term from the list to match each definition.

aquifer	geyser	impermeable	artesian
groundwater	permeable	water table	cave
hot spring	carbonic acid	zone of saturation	spring

_____ **1.** Water that collects underground

_____ **2.** Word describing soil or rock through which water can pass

_____ **3.** Word describing soil or rock through which water cannot pass

_____ **4.** Layer of rock that transmits water freely

_____ **5.** Area where all pores in the rock are filled with water

_____ **6.** Upper surface of the area where all the pores in the rock are filled with water

_____ **7.** Type of well in which water under pressure rises to the surface

_____ **8.** Area where the water table meets Earth's surface and flows out

_____ **9.** Area where heated groundwater comes to the surface

_____ **10.** Hot spring that erupts periodically

_____ **11.** Weak acid that forms when water mixes with carbon dioxide

_____ **12.** Underground opening formed when acid groundwater dissolves limestone

Use the words in the box to fill in the blanks.

calcite	stalactites	evaporates
stalagmites	limestone	

Groundwater continues to affect the _____ rock that forms a cave. It

drips slowly from cracks in the cave walls and ceilings. Sometimes this water

_____ while dripping from the roof of a cave. It leaves deposits of

_____ . These deposits grow down from the cave's ceiling and form

_____ . If the water drips to the cave floor and then evaporates, it leaves

deposits that grow up from the floor. These are called _____ .

Chapter 8

STUDY GUIDE

● Water Wars

Match the definitions in Column I with the terms in Column II. Write the letter of the correct term in the blank on the left.

Column I

_____ 1. Use of water for fishing or boating

_____ 2. Use of water for manufacturing

_____ 3. Change of the natural flow of water

_____ 4. Water that is not salt water

_____ 5. Use of water to grow crops

Column II

a. agricultural use

b. freshwater

c. industrial use

d. water diversion

e. recreational use

Read the sentences that follow and unscramble the terms.

1. When the natural flow of water is changed by people, it is called **trewa verdision**. _____

_____

2. As the population grows, greater demand is put on Earth's **rewfserath** supply. _____

_____

3. One reason people divert water is because they have a water **gheators**. _____

_____

Answer the following questions on the lines provided.

1. What change in population has made some people think about diverting water from the Great

   Lakes? _____

   _____

2. How would that water diversion affect the states on the Great Lakes? _____

   _____

   _____

Chapter 8

STUDY GUIDE

• Ocean Shoreline

Each numbered list below gives some characteristics of one of the shoreline features in the box. Write the name of each shoreline feature above the correct list.

shoreline	beach	longshore current
rocky shoreline	barrier islands	

1. _____

   • rocks
   • cliffs
   • caves

2. _____

   • colliding waves
   • running water
   • parallel to shore

3. _____

   • high tide
   • low tide
   • water's edge

4. _____

   • sand deposits
   • separated from mainland
   • dunes

5. _____

   • smooth, gently sloping
   • sediment deposits
   • sands

A cause is something that makes something happen. An effect is what happens. Write the part of the statement that is the cause and the part that is the effect on the lines provided.

1. Shorelines change constantly because they experience the forces of tides, waves, and currents.

   cause: _____

   effect: _____

2. When constant wave motion bumps sand grains together, the corners of the sand become rounded.

   cause: _____

   effect: _____

3. The more energy a longshore current has, the more it will erode shoreline sediments.

   cause: _____

   effect: _____

4. Beaches have sand-sized particles because waves break rocks and seashells down.

   cause: _____

   effect: _____

Chapter 9

STUDY GUIDE

● Forces Inside Earth

On the line above each illustration, label the type of fault shown—normal fault, reverse fault, and strike-slip fault. Then below each illustration put the numbers of the fault's characteristics from the list.

1. Tension pulls rocks apart.

2. Compression pushes rocks in.

3. Shearing forces push rocks from different, but not opposite, directions.

4. This kind of fault occurs at transform fault boundaries.

5. This kind of fault occurs at divergent plate boundaries.

6. This kind of fault occurs at convergent plate boundaries.

7. Rocks above the fault surface are forced up and over the rocks below the fault surface.

8. Rocks above the fault surface move downward in relation to rocks below the fault surface.

9. Rocks on either side of the fault boundary move past each other without much upward or downward movement.

10. Many of these faults occurred when the Sierra Nevadas were formed.

11. The Himalaya Mountains contain many of these faults.

12. The San Andreas Fault is an example of this kind of fault.

13. Rocks become twisted and strained when they snag each other.

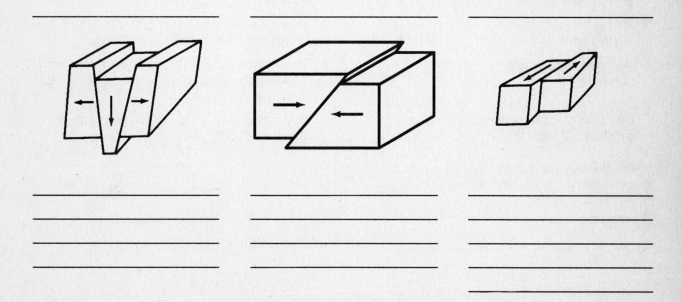

● Earthquake Information

Solve the crossword puzzle by using the clues provided.

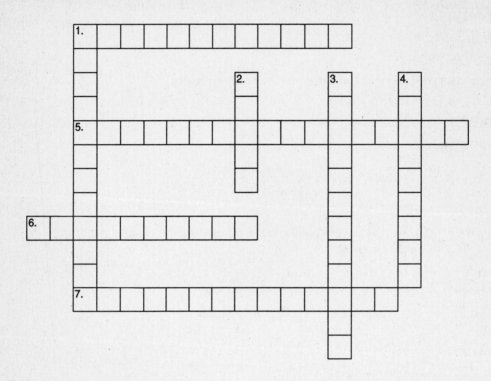

Across

1. These move by giving particles a circular motion and are generated by energy that travels outward from the epicenter. (2 words)

5. This is the name for the boundary between Earth's crust and the upper mantle. (2 words)

6. Area where no seismic waves are detected (2 words)

7. These move through Earth by causing particles to move at right angles to the waves' direction. (2 words)

Identify points A and B on the illustration. One is the epicenter of an earthquake, and one is the focus.

A. _____

B. _____

Down

1. These are forms of energy that are produced at an earthquake's point of origin and travel outward. (2 words)

2. This is the point in Earth's interior where the energy of an earthquake is released.

3. These cause particles to move back and forth in the same direction the waves are moving. (2 words)

4. This is the point on Earth's surface directly above an earthquake's point of origin.

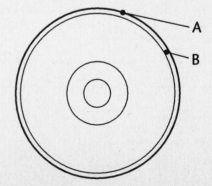

Chapter 9
STUDY GUIDE
● Destruction by Earthquakes

Rewrite each sentence by changing the italicized word or words to make the sentence correct.

1. A *Richter Scale* is an instrument that is used to record primary, secondary, and surface waves of an earthquake. _____

   _____

2. An earthquake's *severity* is the measure of the energy released by the earthquake. _____

   _____

3. Seismic sea waves are also called *secondary waves*. _____

   _____

4. A scientist who studies earthquakes is a *seismograph*. _____

   _____

5. Scientists use the *Moho Scale* to measure the magnitude of earthquakes. _____

6. The earthquake in Kansu, China, registered 8.5 on the Richter Scale and released *ten* times more energy that the one in Messina, Italy, that registered 7.5. _____

   _____

   _____

7. An earthquake that registers between 8.0 and 8.9 on the Richter Scale is likely to happen *about five times* a year. _____

   _____

8. To help make your home earthquake safe, place *heavy objects* on the highest shelves. _____

   _____

   _____

9. An earthquake with a magnitude of 6.7 would release 32 times more energy than an earthquake with a *magnitude of 7.7.* _____

   _____

10. In a year, you could expect *about 6000* earthquakes with magnitude between 1.0 and 3.9.

    _____

    _____

Chapter 9

STUDY GUIDE

● Living on a Fault

Use the terms in the box to complete the sentences.

seismic-safe	earthquake	magnitudes
building codes	vibrations	crumbling structures
San Francisco Bay	highways	underground pipes

1. An _____ can result in the loss of life and great damage to structures built by people.

2. Most deaths occur when people are trapped in or on _____ .

3. Much of the Pacific Coast including the _____ area is earthquake-prone.

4. As a result, California has enforced strict _____ for new construction.

5. The codes have requirements to make new buildings _____ structures.

6. Today many high-rise office buildings stand on steel and rubber springs that help the building ride out the _____ caused by earthquakes.

7. _____ are being built with reinforcing rods in their cement columns.

8. Lives and property could be saved by replacing old _____ for gas and water with new ones that will bend during an earthquake.

9. By having seismic-safe structures, the San Francisco Bay area did not experience as much loss of life as other areas that had earthquakes with similar _____ .

Answer the following questions in complete sentences.

1. What do the San Francisco Bay area, Armenia, and Iran have in common? _____

_____

2. How are highway pillars with spiral reinforcing rods wrapped around them and buildings standing on steel and rubber springs alike? _____

3. Why did Interstate 880 collapse during the earthquake in the San Francisco Bay area? _____

_____

_____

4. Why did California enforce stricter building codes? _____

_____

_____

Chapter 10
STUDY GUIDE

• **Volcanoes and Earth's Moving Plates**

Text Pages 266–273

Write the term or phrase that matches each definition below. Use the letters in the boxes to answer Item 14.

1. ☐ __ __ __ __ __
2. ☐ __ __ __
3. __ ☐ __ __ __ __
4. __ ☐ __ __ __
5. __ __ __ __ __ ☐
6. __ __ __ ☐ __ __ __
7. __ __ __ __ ☐ __   __ __ __ __ __
8. __ ☐ __ __ __ __
9. __ __ __ ☐ __ __ __ __ __ __
10. __ __ __ ☐ __ __
11. __ __ __ __ ☐ __ __ __ __ __
12. __ __ __ __ __ ☐ __
13. __ __ __ __ __ ☐

1. Structures in Earth that move on the asthenosphere

2. Magma that flows out onto Earth's surface

3. Opening at the top of a volcano's vent

4. Long, deep cracks formed when plates separate

5. The state of volcanoes currently spewing smoke, ash, steam, cinders, and/or lava

6. The state of volcanoes not currently active

7. Area around Pacific Plate where earthquakes and volcanoes are common, the Pacific _____

8. Openings in Earth's crust that allow magma to reach the surface

9. Type of boundary where plates separate

10. Melted rock deep inside Earth

11. Type of boundary where one plate slides under another plate

12. Mountain formed from layers of lava and volcanic ash

13. Area in Earth's mantle hot enough to melt rock into magma and create volcanoes

14. What process helps in the formation of volcanoes? _____

Chapter 10

STUDY GUIDE

● Energy from Earth

Answer the following questions on the lines provided.

1. Define geothermal energy. _____
   _____
   _____

2. Write the following sentences in the proper sequence to show how geothermal energy from magma is used.

   • Hot water produces steam.
   • Generators make electricity.
   • Magma heats water.
   • Steam spins generators.
   • Magma is very hot.

   (1) _____
   (2) _____
   (3) _____
   (4) _____
   (5) _____

3. Make a list of the advantages and disadvantages of using geothermal energy instead of energy from fossil fuels.

   Advantages
   _____
   _____
   _____

   Disadvantages
   _____
   _____
   _____

4. What are the two main engineering problems in getting energy from hot dry rock?
   _____
   _____
   _____

Chapter 10
STUDY GUIDE

• Eruptions and Forms of Volcanoes

Text Pages 276–286

Solve the crossword puzzle by using the definitions provided as clues.

Across

3. Smallest-sized tephra

6. Type of magma containing a lot of silica and water vapor

8. Volcano made of alternating layers of lava and tephra

10. Volcanic material thrown out during eruptions

11. Substances that affect the explosiveness of volcanic eruptions

Down

1. Steep-sided volcano made of tephra (2 words)

2. Type of magma containing little silica

4. Mineral that affects the thickness of magma

5. Medium-sized tephra

7. Larger-sized tephra

9. Broad volcano made of flat layers of basaltic lava

Answer the question in the space provided.

12. Two important factors determine whether an eruption will be explosive or quiet. What are they?

_____

_____

Chapter 10

STUDY GUIDE

• Igneous Rock Features

In the blank at the left, write the letter of the term or phrase that correctly completes each statement.

_____ 1. Masses of magma that cool underground and form the largest igneous rock bodies are called _____ .
   a. batholiths   **b.** laccoliths

_____ 2. Ship Rock in New Mexico is an example of a _____ .
   a. laccolith   **b.** volcanic neck

_____ 3. Most igneous activity takes place _____ .
   a. underground   **b.** above ground

_____ 4. Magma that squeezes into a horizontal crack and hardens forms a _____ .
   a. dike   **b.** sill

_____ 5. When the top of a volcano collapses into the vent, a _____ is formed.
   a. crater   **b.** caldera

_____ 6. A dome of rock pushed up by a magma sill is a _____ .
   a. batholith   **b.** laccolith

_____ 7. Volcanic features that can sometimes be seen above ground are _____ .
   a. volcanic necks and batholiths **b.** dikes and sills

_____ 8. Magma that squeezes into a vertical crack and hardens forms a _____ .
   a. dike   **b.** sill

_____ 9. Crater Lake in Oregon is an example of a _____ .
   a. dike   **b.** caldera

_____ 10. When erosion wears away the outside of a volcano, sometimes a solid magma core called a _____ is left exposed.
   a. cinder cone   **b.** volcanic neck

_____ 11. The granite domes in Yosemite National Park in California are part of a _____ .
   a. batholith   **b.** sill

_____ 12. Volcanoes are examples of igneous activity _____ .
   a. underground   **b.** above ground

_____ 13. Magma that cools underground forms _____ igneous rock.
   a. extrusive   **b.** intrusive

_____ 14. The difference between dikes and sills is the _____ of their formation.
   a. direction   **b.** size

Chapter 11

STUDY GUIDE

● Continental Drift

Use the words and phrases in the boxes to complete each part of the outline.

Climate clues	Plants
Fossil clues	Rock clues
Glaciers	

Evidence for continental drift

I. Early evidence

   A. Puzzlelike fit of continents

   B. _____

      1. *Mesosaurus*

      2. *Glossopteris*

      3. _____

   C. _____

      1. _____

      2. Glacial deposits

   D. _____

Magnetic evidence	Reversal of magnetic alignment of rocks
Age evidence	Ocean rock younger than continental rock
Older rock farther from mid-ocean ridge	

II. Later evidence: seafloor spreading

   A. _____

      1. *Glomar Challenger* research

         a. Newer rock near mid-ocean ridge

         b. _____

         c. _____

   B. _____

      1. Known reversal of Earth's magnetic field

      2. _____

Chapter 11
STUDY GUIDE

• Seafloor Spreading

Use words in the boxes to fill in the blanks.

inner core	liquid	rock
iron and nickel	outer core	solid

Scientists know Earth's interior is made mostly of layers of _____ .

Some layers, like the center part, called the _____ are hard and

_____ . Other layers are not. The layer next to the center, called the

_____ , is _____ . Both parts of the core are made of

_____ .

continents	mantle	plasticlike
crust	oceans	soil
hot		

The largest layer inside Earth is called the _____ . It's neither completely

solid nor completely liquid, but _____ . It's extremely

_____ .

Earth's outermost layer is the _____ . This layer is about 5 km thick

under the _____ and up to 35 km thick under the

_____ . On top of the outer layer is the weathered rock we call

_____ .

Chapter 11

STUDY GUIDE

● Theory of Plate Tectonics

In the blank at the left, write the letter of the term or phrase that best completes each statement.

_____ 1. The theory that Earth's crust and upper mantle are broken into sections is called _____ .
    a. seafloor spreading   **b.** plate tectonics

_____ 2. Plates are composed of the _____ .
    a. crust and part of the upper mantle   **b.** lithosphere and asthenosphere

_____ 3. The lithosphere is composed of the _____ .
    a. plates and seafloor   **b.** crust and upper mantle

_____ 4. Plates float on the _____ .
    a. asthenosphere   **b.** lithosphere

_____ 5. Plates can _____ .
    a. pull apart, collide, and move past one another   **b.** erupt and form precipitation

_____ 6. The boundary between two plates that are moving apart is a _____ boundary.
    a. convergent   **b.** divergent

_____ 7. When ocean plates collide with continental plates, the denser ocean plate _____ .
    a. sinks   **b.** rises

_____ 8. The area where a plate descends is a _____ .
    a. convergent boundary   **b.** subduction zone

_____ 9. A _____ is created where one plate moves under another.
    a. mantle   **b.** trench

_____ 10. A subducted plate melts, forming _____ .
    a. magma and volcanic mountains   **b.** the lithosphere

_____ 11. Two continental plates may collide and cause _____ .
    a. glaciers   **b.** earthquakes

_____ 12. Scientists think plates are moved by _____ .
    a. convection currents   **b.** volcanoes

_____ 13. A place where plates slide past one another is a _____ .
    a. divergent fault   **b.** transform fault

_____ 14. The San Andreas Fault is a _____ .
    a. volcano   **b.** transform fault

_____ 15. The Himalayas were formed at a _____ .
    a. convergent boundary   **b.** transform fault

Chapter 11

STUDY GUIDE

● Before Pangaea, Rodinia

Complete each statement from your textbook on the lines provided.

1. Edges of some continents look as if they would _____ .

2. People wondered if these continents had been _____ .

3. In 1915, Alfred Wegener proposed an idea called _____ .

4. This idea states that continents moved through the _____ .

5. Wegener thought that long ago the continents formed _____ .

6. He named it Pangaea, which means _____ .

7. Wegener's idea was rejected. The idea was so different that _____

   _____ .

8. Today Wegener's ideas about continental drift are _____ .

9. Today some people still have trouble _____ .

10. One new idea that is still being debated explains _____ .

11. Walter and Luis Alvarez think that a large rocky object _____ .

12. This collision threw _____ .

13. The dust blocked the _____ .

14. This caused _____ .

Answer the questions on the lines provided.

15. Explain how Pangaea fits into Wegener's theory of continental drift. _____

   _____

   _____

16. State one reason why Wegener's ideas about continental drift were not believed.

   _____

   _____

Chapter 12

STUDY GUIDE

● Fossils

Match the terms in Column I with their descriptions in Column II. Write the letter of the correct phrase in the blank at the left.

Column I

_____ 1. fossil

_____ 2. cast

_____ 3. mold

_____ 4. index fossil

_____ 5. carbonaceous film

_____ 6. petrified remain

Column II

a. Fossil from a species that existed on Earth for a short period of time

b. Fossil made from a thin film of carbon atoms and molecules

c. Remain, imprint, or trace of a once-living organism

d. Hard and rocklike fossil

e. Cavity left in rock by a decayed organism

f. Produced when a cavity is filled in with solid matter

Circle the word in the blank that makes the statement correct.

7. (Impressions, Fossils) are preserved remains or traces of life-forms.

8. Organisms have a better chance of being preserved if they have (hard, soft) parts.

9. A hard, rocklike fossil, called a (petrified, trace) fossil develops when minerals fill spaces left when the original substance dissolves.

10. A carbonaceous (decay, film) fossil is made when pressure and heat force out gases and liquids, leaving a thin residue of the organism.

11. A (mold, cast) is made when sediments fill in a cavity and harden.

12. (Original, Carbon) remains have been preserved in frozen ground and in amber.

13. Preserved tracks and other evidence of animal activity are called (index, trace) fossils.

14. Fossils of life-forms that existed on Earth for a short period of time and were widespread geographically are called (index, trace) fossils.

15. Fossils show that the (environment, elevation) of Antarctica has changed greatly.

Chapter 12
STUDY GUIDE

● Extinction of Dinosaurs

Use the words in the boxes to fill in the blanks.

dominant	mammals	160 million	intelligent

Dinosaurs were abundant on Earth's land for about _____ years. These

fast, agile, and _____ animals were the _____ land

animals. Only after the end of their rule did another class of animals, _____ ,

increase.

Alvarez	dinosaurs	extinct	western
iridium	dust	meteorite	66 million
collision	theory		

The remains of _____ have been found in the

_____ part of the United States. These great animals have been

_____ for about _____ years. Two scientists, Luis

and Walter _____ , have uncovered traces of _____ in

rock layers. They now think they know why the animals died. Their _____

is that Earth and a _____ from space had a _____ .

This raised _____ , which dimmed the sun's light. The meteorite's impact

would also account for the iridium deposit.

mineral	photosynthesis	temperature	volcanic activity

The meteorite collision has been rejected by some scientists who think increased

_____ is a more likely theory. Either event would explain the presence of the

rare _____ iridium and would have resulted in a dimming of the sun. This

would kill plants that depend on the sun for _____ and would lower Earth's

_____ .

Chapter 12

STUDY GUIDE

● Relative Ages of Rocks

In the blank at the left, write the letter of the term or phrase that best completes each statement.

_____ 1. In layers of undisturbed sedimentary rock, the oldest rocks are on the _____ .
   a. top   **b.** bottom

_____ 2. Sediments deposited in layers form _____ rocks.
   a. sedimentary   **b.** igneous

_____ 3. The statement that old rocks are on the bottom in layers of undisturbed rock is called the
   _____ .
   a. principle of superposition   **b.** tectonic theory

_____ 4. Sometimes layers of rock are overturned by forces generated by _____ .
   a. superposition   **b.** tectonic activity

_____ 5. Determining the age of rocks by examining their position in a layer is called _____ .
   a. relative dating   **b.** faulting

_____ 6. Gaps in rock layers are called _____ .
   a. faults   **b.** unconformities

_____ 7. The type of unconformity in which an erosional surface exists in one of several horizontal
   layers is called a(n) _____ .
   a. angular unconformity   **b.** disconformity

_____ 8. Matching of rock layers in two different areas is called _____ the layers.
   a. concluding   **b.** correlating

_____ 9. One way to match rock layers that are apart is to see if the same type of _____ are found
   in both places.
   a. fossils   **b.** water

_____ 10. Sometimes rock layers are visible because they have been exposed by _____ cutting
   through them.
   a. volcanoes   **b.** streams

_____ 11. Some unconformities are the result of _____ .
   a. erosion   **b.** volcanoes

12. Number the rock layers according to their relative ages. Label the oldest rock type #1.

   A. _____
   B. _____
   C. _____
   D. _____
   E. _____
   F. _____

Chapter 12
STUDY GUIDE

• Absolute Ages of Rocks

Use the words in the boxes to fill in the blanks.

absolute dating	element	neutrons
age	isotopes	radioactive
atoms	lead-206	uranium-238

Besides relative dating, geologists use another method to determine in years the

_____ of rocks and other objects. It's called _____ .

It's a process that uses the properties of the _____ in objects.

Elements can have atoms with different numbers of _____ in their nuclei.

Some of these _____ undergo a process of _____

decay. When the isotope decays, a new _____ is formed. An example of this

decay is the change of the isotope _____ to _____ .

carbon-14	nitrogen-14	radiometric dating
daughter product	parent material	uniformitarianism
half-life		

Another example of decaying isotopes is the isotope _____ , which

decays to _____ . The original isotope in this process is called the

_____ . The isotope that results from the decay is the

_____ .

Every radioactive _____ has a certain rate at which it decays to its

_____ . This rate is known as its _____ .

Calculating the absolute age of a rock is called _____ . Long before this

was possible, a Scottish scientist estimated that Earth was millions of years old. He used the principle

called _____ , which states that Earth's processes occurring today are similar

to those that occurred in the past.

Chapter 13

STUDY GUIDE   • **Evolution and Geologic Time**

Use the words in the box to fill in the blanks in the statements.

adapted	continents	environment	extinct
epochs	eras	fossils	plate tectonics
geologic time scale	natural selection	organic evolution	periods
species			

1. The division of Earth's history into units makes up the _____ .

2. Major divisions of Earth's history are _____ .

3. Each major division may be divided into _____ .

4. The Cenozoic Era is divided into _____ .

5. Clues to which organisms lived in different eras are found in _____ .

6. A gradual change in life-forms over time is _____ .

7. Each change in Earth created different surroundings for organisms, these surroundings are called their _____ .

8. A group of organisms that normally reproduce only among themselves is a _____ .

9. After major changes in Earth's environments, species either died out or _____ .

10. Species that could not adapt to changes eventually became _____ .

11. Organisms with traits that are suited to an environment survive by the process of _____ .

12. At different times in Earth's history, plate tectonics caused collision and separation of _____ .

13. Many species adapted or became extinct because _____ caused their environments to change when the continents collided or separated.

Chapter 13

STUDY GUIDE

• Present-Day Rapid Extinctions

Read each statement, and then answer the questions in complete sentences.

1. Throughout Earth's history species have become extinct. What causes extinction?

   _____

   _____

2. The activities of humans living about 10 000 years ago may have caused some extinctions. How do present-day humans affect animal species? _____

   _____

3. How might economic development in a city or suburb affect the habitat of birds that are in the area? _____

   _____

4. Tropical rain forests contain 50 to 80 percent of Earth's species. What has been done to threaten these species? _____

   _____

5. Organisms need a place to live, grow, and interact with each other and their environment. What is such a place called? _____

6. Habitats are being destroyed in many places. What may happen to the organisms that live in these habitats? _____

7. Some species that still exist are endangered. What does *endangered* mean? _____

   _____

8. Some people want to save habitats by restricting construction and planning projects so habitats are disturbed as little as possible. What are these people trying to slow down? _____

9. Some medicines and other products come from various organisms. Why might this be a reason to try to save organisms? _____

   _____

Chapter 13
STUDY GUIDE

• Early Earth History

Answer the questions on the lines at the left.

_____ 1. Which era or "time" in the geologic time scale lasted the longest?

_____ 2. Which era or "time" is the oldest?

_____ 3. What is thought to be one of the earliest forms of life on Earth?

_____ 4. What appeared in the atmosphere that allowed more complex organisms to develop?

_____ 5. What kind of animals developed near the end of the first era?

_____ 6. What name was given to the second of Earth's eras?

_____ 7. What covered most of Earth's surface at the beginning of the second era?

_____ 8. What familiar marine life-form evolved during this era?

_____ 9. What type of animal evolved that lived out of water but reproduced in water?

_____ 10. What mountain chain was caused by the collision of the Eurasian or African continental plates with the North American Plate?

_____ 11. What type of animal is thought to have developed after the evolution of an egg that would not dry out on land?

_____ 12. The formation of swamps and the decay of swamp vegetation are the basis for what fossil fuel?

Answer the following questions in complete sentences on the lines provided.

13. What happened to all of the continental plates near the end of the Paleozoic Era? _____

_____

_____

14. What happened to many land and sea animals at this time? _____

_____

Chapter 13

STUDY GUIDE

Text Pages 374–382

• Middle and Recent Earth History

Determine whether each of the following statements is true or false. Write "true" in the blank at the left if the statement is true. For each false statement, write a word or phrase to replace the italicized word or phrase to make the statement true.

_____ 1. The first dinosaurs appeared in the *Triassic* Period.

_____ 2. By the *Jurassic* Period, large dinosaurs lived on Earth.

_____ 3. The word *Laurasia* refers to the era of middle life.

_____ 4. In this era, Pangaea began to *come together*.

_____ 5. Some dinosaurs ate *meat*.

_____ 6. One part of Pangaea was *Gondwanaland*.

_____ 7. Modern-day reptiles are *cold-blooded*.

_____ 8. It's now believed that dinosaurs may have been *warm-blooded*.

_____ 9. An *Archeotopteryx* was similar to both dinosaurs and birds.

_____ 10. A warm-blooded vertebrate that has hair or fur and that produces milk to feed its young is a *reptile*.

_____ 11. At the end of the Mesozoic Era, volcanoes were very *active*.

_____ 12. A plant with naked seeds is a(n) *angiosperm*.

_____ 13. A plant producing seeds with hard outer coverings is a(n) *angiosperm*.

_____ 14. The *Cenozoic Era* is the era of recent life.

_____ 15. The Cenozoic Era began when dinosaurs *grew to be large*.

_____ 16. Early species of mammals evolved into *smaller* life-forms.

_____ 17. Life-forms became isolated when the continents began to *break up*.

_____ 18. About 10 000 years ago, *dinosaurs* became a dominant land animal.

_____ 19. Early *humans* may have caused the extinction of some other animals.

_____ 20. Many *North American* mammals are marsupials.

Chapter 14
STUDY GUIDE

● Earth's Atmosphere

In the blank at the left, write the letter of the term in Column II that matches each definition in Column I.

Column I

_____ 1. Layer of atmosphere where weather, clouds, and smog occur

_____ 2. Force of air determined by temperature and distance above sea level

_____ 3. Naturally occurring gas in the stratosphere that is considered a pollutant in the lower atmosphere

_____ 4. Layer of the thermosphere that has a high concentration of electrically charged particles

_____ 5. Most common gas in the atmosphere

_____ 6. Layer of atmosphere that includes the ozone layer

_____ 7. Type of pollution that can be formed by car exhaust and burning coal or oil

_____ 8. Layer of atmosphere between the thermosphere and space

Column II

a. air pressure

b. ionosphere

c. nitrogen

d. ozone

e. smog

f. stratosphere

g. exosphere

h. troposphere

In the blank, write the term that correctly completes each sentence. Use the information in your textbook.

9. _____ makes up from 0 to 4 percent of the atmosphere.

10. The _____ contains 75 percent of the atmospheric gases.

11. The division of Earth's atmosphere into layers is based on _____ differences.

12. Cold air is denser than warm air and, therefore, has higher _____ .

13. _____ is the only substance that exists as a solid, liquid, and gas in Earth's atmosphere.

Identify the five main layers of Earth's atmosphere.

Atmosphere {
E _____
D _____
C _____
B _____
A _____
Earth
}

14. A is the _____ .

15. B is the _____ .

16. C is the _____ .

17. D is the _____ .

18. E is the _____ .

Chapter 14

STUDY GUIDE

● The Ozone Layer

Choose the correct term in the box and write each term after its definition.

chlorofluorocarbons	ozone layer	ultraviolet radiation

1. Layer in the stratosphere containing ozone, which absorbs ultraviolet radiation

   _____

2. Type of energy from the sun that can be harmful in large amounts

   _____

3. Chemicals used in some aerosol sprays, refrigerants, and some foam products

   _____

Determine whether each of the following statements is true or false. Write the word "true" or "false" in the blank. If the statement is false, rewrite it so that it's true.

_____ 4. The kind of oxygen we breathe can absorb ultraviolet radiation.

   _____

   _____

_____ 5. If the ozone layer disappeared, cancer rates would be much higher than they are now.

   _____

   _____

_____ 6. Chlorofluorocarbons are making the ozone layer thicker.

   _____

   _____

_____ 7. The ozone layer acts as a shield between us and ultraviolet radiation.

   _____

   _____

_____ 8. A thick, unchanging layer of ozone covers the entire Earth.

   _____

   _____

_____ 9. Ozone molecules destroy chlorofluorocarbon molecules.

   _____

   _____

Chapter 14

STUDY GUIDE

● Energy from the Sun

Use the words in the box to fill in the blanks.

heat	life	absorb	radiation
sun	lower	reflects	density
waves	current	contact	conduction
sinks	campfire	environment	temperature
space	surfaces	atmosphere	convection

The _____ is the source of all energy in our atmosphere. When Earth

receives this energy, some energy escapes back into _____ , some is absorbed

by the _____ , and some is absorbed by land and water

_____ . The balance among these three help the atmosphere support

_____ . Energy reaches Earth in the form of radiant energy, or

_____ . This process is the transfer of energy by _____ .

You experience radiation when you sit by a _____ and your skin becomes

warm. The molecules of your skin _____ the energy and you feel

_____ . Heat is the transfer of energy from an object with a higher

_____ to an object with a _____ temperature. Some

radiation isn't absorbed by the atmosphere or surface objects; it _____ off

the atmosphere or surface.

_____ is the transfer of energy that occurs when molecules bump

into one another and heat is transferred through direct _____ .

_____ is the transfer of heat that occurs because of

_____ differences in the air. Because cold air has a higher density than warm

air, cold air _____—this pushes up the warm air. This rise and fall of air sets

up a circular movement called a convection _____ . Convection currents and

other processes that transfer energy help provide the _____ we live in.

Chapter 14

STUDY GUIDE

• Movement of Air

Use the diagrams below to identify the following terms: doldrums, land breeze, polar easterlies, prevailing westerlies, trade winds, sea breeze. Write each term next to the appropriate number.

1. _____

2. _____

3. _____

4. _____

5. _____

6. _____

7. _____

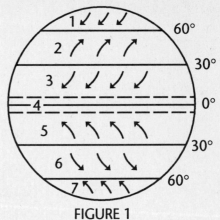

FIGURE 1

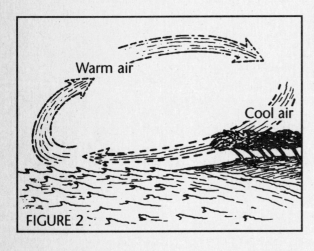

FIGURE 2

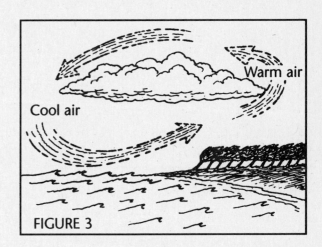

FIGURE 3

8. _____   9. _____

In the blank on the left, write the term that matches each definition.

_____ **10.** The turning of air masses from their original paths because of Earth's rotation

_____ **11.** High altitude winds that occur in places where trade winds and polar easterlies meet prevailing westerlies

_____ **12.** Air movement patterns on Earth's surface as shown in Figure 1

_____ **13.** Circular movement of air that causes the winds shown in Figure 2

Chapter 15

STUDY GUIDE

● What Is Weather?

In the word search puzzle, find and circle the word that completes each sentence. Write the word on the line.

1. The present state of the atmosphere is the _____ .

2. _____ is the amount of water vapor in the air.

3. Air is _____ when it is holding all the moisture it can at a certain temperature.

4. The temperature at which air is saturated and condensation begins is the _____ point.

5. _____ humidity is the amount of water vapor in air compared to the amount of water vapor air can hold at a certain temperature.

6. A _____ is an instrument that measures relative humidity.

7. When millions of tiny drops of water around dust particles form from condensed humid air, a _____ forms.

8. A stratus cloud that forms near the ground is _____ .

9. Water droplets that become too heavy to remain suspended in the air fall out of the clouds as _____ .

10. _____ forms when water drops freeze in layers around small nuclei of ice.

11. Water drops that fall when the temperature is above freezing fall as _____ .

12. Water drops that fall when the temperature is below freezing fall as _____ .

13. When snow passes through warm air, melts, and refreezes near the ground, it becomes _____ .

```
T  S  A  T  U  R  A  T  E  D  F  Q  Y  M  B

B  N  O  P  S  Y  C  H  R  O  M  E  T  E  R

Y  O  W  Q  L  N  W  G  A  V  H  R  L  F  I

A  W  P  R  E  C  I  P  I  T  A  T  I  O  N

J  D  B  C  E  I  T  C  N  U  I  L  N  G  A

R  E  L  A  T  I  V  E  X  C  L  O  U  D  C

K  W  U  B  L  H  U  M  I  D  I  T  Y  U  V

Y  J  W  E  A  T  H  E  R  G  M  R  O  M  A
```

Chapter 15

STUDY GUIDE

• Weather Patterns

Fill in the sentence outline using information from Section 15-2 in your textbook.

I. Changes in Weather

A. An air mass is _____

_____

B. A front is _____

_____

    1. A warm front develops when _____

_____

    2. A cold front forms when _____

_____

    3. A stationary front forms when _____

_____

    4. An occluded front results when _____

_____

II. Pressure Systems

A. High pressure systems generally mean clear weather because _____

_____

B. Low pressure systems generally mean cloudy weather because _____

_____

III. Severe Weather

A. Thunderstorms result from _____

_____

B. Tornadoes occur in thunderstorms when _____

_____

_____

_____

C. Hurricanes are _____

_____

Chapter 15

STUDY GUIDE

● Forecasting Weather

In the blank at the left, write the letter of the term in Column II that matches each definition in Column I.

Column I

_____ 1. Advisory to prepare for severe weather

_____ 2. Person who studies the weather

_____ 3. Average of all weather conditions of an area over a long period

_____ 4. Weather information at a specific location

_____ 5. Line connecting points of equal temperature on a weather map

_____ 6. Regions on Earth that have cold winters, hot summers, and mild springs and falls

_____ 7. Advisory that severe weather conditions exist

_____ 8. Regions on Earth that have hot temperatures all year

_____ 9. Line connecting points of equal atmospheric pressure on a weather map

_____ 10. Regions on Earth extending from the poles to 66 1/2° north and south latitudes

Column II

a. climate

b. meteorologist

c. isobar

d. isotherm

e. station model

f. temperate zones

g. polar zones

h. tropical zones

i. watch

j. warning

Answer the following questions on the lines provided.

11. What do you do if a watch is issued? If a warning is issued? _____

_____

_____

_____

_____

12. How do meteorologists gather weather information? _____

_____

_____

13. What can isobars tell you about wind speed? _____

_____

_____

_____

Chapter 15

Text Pages 444–459

STUDY GUIDE

• Changing the Weather

Answer the questions below on the lines provided.

1. List several human activities that alter the weather. _____
_____
_____

2. Why is the air over cities usually warmer than the air over rural areas? _____
_____
_____

3. What are the two main conditions that some scientists hypothesize are needed for successful cloud
seeding? _____
_____

4. Why have many cloud seeding experiments failed? _____
_____

5. What are two methods used for cloud seeding? _____
_____

6. What is the potential danger in seeding clouds to reduce hurricane wind speeds? _____
_____

7. At what size does a particle and its added ice crystals fall from a cloud as precipitation? _____
_____

8. What are three examples of when cloud seeding experiments have been successful? _____
_____
_____

Chapter 16

STUDY GUIDE

• What Is Climate?

Determine whether each statement below is true or false. Write "true" in the blank at the left if the statement is true. For each false statement, write a word or phrase to replace the italicized word or phrase to make the statement true.

_____ 1. *Tropical* regions receive the most solar radiation.

_____ 2. Water heats up and cools down *faster* than land.

_____ 3. Winds blowing from the sea contain *more* moisture than winds blowing from the land.

_____ 4. Temperatures in a large city are generally *lower* than temperatures in the surrounding rural areas.

_____ 5. There are *more* air molecules to absorb heat emitted by Earth's surface at higher elevations than at sea level.

_____ 6. Deserts are common on the side of a mountain *facing* the wind.

_____ 7. Year-round temperatures in *temperate zones* are always hot, except at high elevations.

_____ 8. As air *rises*, it cools down.

Answer the following questions on the lines provided.

9. What are three weather conditions that are considered in determining a region's climate?

_____

_____

10. What are four factors that affect the climate of a region? _____

_____

_____

Chapter 16
STUDY GUIDE

● Climate Types

Use the terms in the box to complete the sentences.

climatologists	vegetation	wet	behavioral
ferns	semiarid	hibernation	
adaptations	continental	estivation	

1. Some mammals undergo a period of inactivity in winter called _____ .

2. Changes in activity that help organisms survive in a certain environment are _____ adaptations.

3. Dry climates are divided into _____ and arid.

4. Where there is heavy rainfall, some typical plants are moss-draped trees and _____ .

5. People who study climates are called _____ .

6. _____ is an inactive state through which lungfish survive periods of intense heat.

7. Most _____ climates are found between latitudes 30° north and 30° south.

8. Characteristics that organisms develop over a long time that help them survive are called _____ .

9. One of the six climate groups in the Köppen Climate Classification System is the _____ climate.

10. The type of _____ in a region depends on the climate.

Complete the following item on the lines provided.

11. List the six climate groups in the Köppen Climate Classification System.

_____

_____

_____

_____

_____

_____

Chapter 16

STUDY GUIDE

● Climatic Changes

In the blank, write the letter of the term or phrase that best completes each statement.

_____ 1. The farther from the equator, the _____ the hours of daylight vary during the year.
    a. more   **b.** less

_____ 2. El Niño affects the world's weather _____ .
    a. during the summer months   **b.** for a period of time longer than three months

_____ 3. Catastrophic events that have affected Earth's climate in the past include _____ .
    a. volcanic eruptions   **b.** glaciation

_____ 4. Ice sheets formed when the temperature of Earth was higher have _____ concentrations of carbon dioxide.
    a. smaller   **b.** greater

_____ 5. _____ causes the seasons.
    a. a change in Earth's orbit   **b.** the tilt of Earth's axis

Answer the following questions on the lines provided.

6. What are some of the major kinds of evidence that Earth's climate differed in the past?

_____

_____

7. How do meteorite impacts affect Earth's climate? _____

_____

8. Why might the movement of the plates in Earth's crust affect the climate? _____

_____

_____

9. How did the eruption of Mount Pinatubo in 1991 affect Earth's climate? _____

_____

10. What effects would an increase in clouds have on Earth's climate? _____

_____

_____

Chapter 16
STUDY GUIDE

Text Pages 470–475

• How Can Global Warming Be Slowed?

Match the words in Column I with the phrases in Column II. Write the letter of the correct phrase in the blank on the left.

Column I

_____ **1.** fossil fuels

_____ **2.** deforestation

_____ **3.** burning

_____ **4.** plants

_____ **5.** giant screen

_____ **6.** nitrous oxide

Column II

a. remove carbon dioxide from atmosphere

b. possible way to reduce global warming

c. mass removal of trees

d. adds carbon dioxide to atmosphere

e. gas that contributes to global warming

f. petroleum, natural gas, and coal

Answer the following questions on the lines provided.

7. What are some of the ways that people can reduce their use of fossil fuels? _____

_____

_____

_____

_____

8. What are examples of reasons why forests are being cleared in different parts of the world?

_____

_____

_____

_____

9. How can planting vegetation help reduce global warming? _____

_____

_____

_____

10. Why have some scientists suggested that billions of aluminum balloons should be released into

the atmosphere? _____

_____

_____

_____

Chapter 17

STUDY GUIDE

● Ocean Water

Use the words in the box to complete the statements.

volcanoes	basins	iron
halite	salinity	chlorine

1. Billions of years ago, low areas on Earth called _____ filled with water to form oceans.

2. Besides sodium, _____ is the most abundant element in seawater.

3. The _____ of seawater is a measure of the amount of solids dissolved in it.

4. Scientists hypothesize that water vapor from _____ accumulated in Earth's early atmosphere and caused torrential rains to fall.

5. The salt used to flavor food is called _____ .

6. One example of an element that forms a solid and falls to the ocean floor is

_____ .

Answer the following questions on the lines provided.

7. Where do the salts that are dissolved in seawater come from? _____

_____

_____

8. How do living things affect the amount of calcium and silica in the oceans? _____

_____

_____

9. How do volcanoes affect the composition of the oceans? _____

_____

_____

10. What are some of the ways in which oceans affect life on land? _____

_____

_____

Chapter 17

Text Pages 484–489

STUDY GUIDE

● Ocean Currents

Write answers on the lines provided.

1. What currents are influenced by the Coriolis effect? _____

2. Where surface currents carry water away from an area, an upwelling may occur. What is it that "wells up"? What does it carry with it? _____
_____

3. Is the Gulf Stream a surface current or a density current? _____

4. What kind of water movement helps the fishing industry? How? _____
_____

5. Explain how understanding the Gulf Stream helped eighteenth century sailing ships travel more rapidly from America to England. _____
_____
_____

6. Which coasts of continents tend to be warmer, the eastern or the western? Explain. _____
_____

7. On the map below, draw an arrow to represent the Gulf Stream and label it.

8. On the map, draw an arrow representing the South Equatorial Current west of South America and label it.

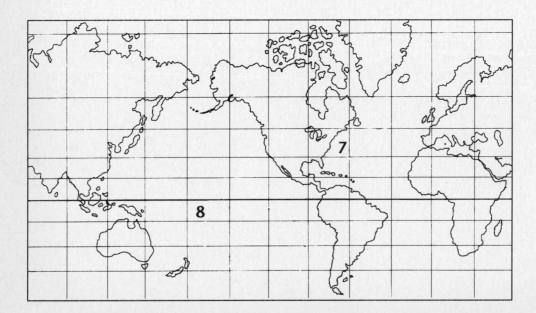

Chapter 17

STUDY GUIDE

● Ocean Waves and Tides

Match the items in Column I with the terms in Column II. Write the letter on the blank at the left.

Column I

_____ 1. Force exerted by objects on every other object

_____ 2. Exerts a strong pull on water in the ocean

_____ 3. Movement in which water, whether in an ocean, lake, or swimming pool, alternately rises and falls

_____ 4. Difference between high and low tide

_____ 5. Created by the collapse of a wave

_____ 6. Highest point of a wave

_____ 7. A rise and fall in the surface level of the ocean caused by a giant wave

_____ 8. When high tides are higher and low tides are lower than normal

_____ 9. Vertical distance between a wave's crest and trough

_____ 10. Horizontal distance between crests of successive waves

_____ 11. Lowest point of a wave

_____ 12. When high tides are lower and low tides are higher than normal

Column II

a. breaker

b. neap tide

c. crest

d. gravity

e. spring tide

f. tidal range

g. tide

h. trough

i. moon

j. wave

k. wave height

l. wavelength

13. Label Figures 1–4 as either *spring tide* or *neap tide*.

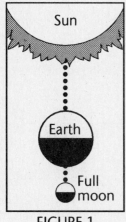

FIGURE 1

FIGURE 2

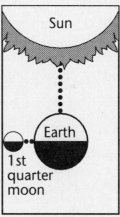

FIGURE 3

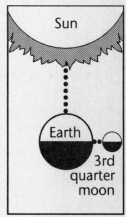

FIGURE 4

_____   _____   _____   _____

Chapter 17

STUDY GUIDE

● Tapping Tidal Energy

Answer the following questions on the lines provided.

1. Where is a tidal power plant planned? _____

_____

2. Average tidal ranges throughout the world are between 0.5 and 3 meters. Explain why the Bay of Fundy is a better than average place to build a tidal power plant. _____

_____

_____

3. What would hold back the water after the Bay of Fundy tide has come in? _____

_____

4. What would the outgoing water pass over as it leaves the dam? _____

_____

5. How would the Bay of Fundy power plant produce electricity? _____

_____

6. List advantages of the Bay of Fundy power plant. _____

_____

_____

7. List disadvantages of the Bay of Fundy power plant. _____

_____

_____

_____

8. Explain how the Bay of Fundy power plant could bring more jobs while destroying others.

_____

_____

Chapter 18

STUDY GUIDE   ● **The Seafloor**

Write the term that matches each description below on the spaces provided. Then complete Item 9.

1. __ E __ __ __ __ __ __ __

2. __ __ __ __ __ __ __ __ L __ __ __

3. __ O __ __ __ __ __ __ __ __ __ __ __ __ __ __

4. __ __ A __ __ __ __ __ __ __ __ __ __ __ __

5. __ __ __ __ __ __ __ __ __ __ __ __ __ __ F

6. __ __ __ __ __ __ __ S __

7. __ R __ __ __ __

8. __ __ __ - O __ __ __ __ __ __ __

1. Inactive volcano found on the ocean floor

2. Flat seafloor in the deep ocean formed when deposits of sediment filled valleys

3. Area at the end of the continental shelf

4. Sediments found where rivers meet oceans

5. Gently sloping part of the continent that extends underwater

6. Mineral concentrated with nickel and cobalt in nodules found across 20 to 50 percent of the Pacific basin

7. Deep ocean valley that forms where one part of the seafloor is pushed beneath another part

8. Underwater mountain chains that form when forces within Earth cause the seafloor to spread apart

9. Write the letters in the boxes on the lines provided. Then unscramble the letters to complete the sentence that follows.

__ __ __ __ __ __ __ __

All of the features identified in this activity are part of the _____.

Chapter 18

STUDY GUIDE

● Life in the Ocean

Find the term for each clue in the puzzle and circle it. The terms may read across or down. Then write the term after the clue.

1. Group of ocean life that includes larger animals that swim _____

2. Gas used in the process of photosynthesis _____

3. Used with sunlight and carbon dioxide by plants in photosynthesis _____

4. Colony of corals _____

5. Needed in photosynthesis but not in chemosynthesis _____

6. Example of an animal plankton _____

7. Process by which plants produce food and oxygen _____

8. Animal in the nekton group that roams the entire ocean _____

9. Benthos that creates a hard calcium outer covering _____

10. Food-chain process that takes place along the mid-ocean ridges and does not require sunlight _____

11. Example of plant plankton _____

12. Group made up of drifting plants and animals _____

13. Gas used in respiration and released in photosynthesis _____

14. Group made up of organisms that live on the ocean floor _____

15. Example of nekton _____

```
O C A R B O N D I O X I D E
P H O T O S Y N T H E S I S
T R E S P I R A T I O N N U
U C E A W R E E F N L O E N
R I F E H C O R A L A X K L
T N D I A T O M S D L Y T I
L I F P L A N K T O N G O G
E E P B E N T H O S R E N H
S O J E L L Y F I S H N C T
C H E M O S Y N T H E S I S
E S N U T R I E N T S S E S
```

Chapter 18

STUDY GUIDE

• Pollution and Marine Life

Use the terms in the box to complete the sentences in the following paragraphs.

soil sediments	solid wastes	industrial waste
plankton	oil spills	food chains
pollution	herbicides	organisms

When harmful waste products, chemicals, and substances get into an environment,

_____ occurs. Humans can pollute the ocean in many ways. Most ocean

pollution is located along the coasts of the continents. Manufacturers may release

_____ like chemicals and metals. People use pesticides, including

_____, that enter the ocean through runoff. People can carelessly dispose of

such _____ as plastic bags and plastic beverage can rings. Leaks in offshore

oil wells or tanker collisions can lead to _____ . Even

_____ from plowed fields can pollute the ocean environment.

When an ocean becomes polluted, the effects are felt far beyond the water's limits. There is

disruption of _____, and there can be severe effects on Earth's oxygen

supply, much of which is produced by _____. All these forms of human

pollution can cause the death of many _____ not only in the ocean but

throughout Earth.

For each type of pollution of the ocean identified, number the events that harm ocean organisms in the order that they happen.

A. Pollution by human sewage

_____ Bacteria use up oxygen needed by other organisms and those organisms die.

_____ The sewage fertilizes the water.

_____ Human sewage flows into the ocean.

_____ Bacteria decompose the plankton when they die.

_____ Some plankton reproduce more quickly because of the fertilized water.

B. Pollution by soil runoff

_____ The filter-feeding systems of oysters and clams become clogged.

_____ Human activities tear up the soil.

_____ Silt accumulates in coastal areas.

_____ Rain washes the soil into streams and eventually into the ocean.

Chapter 19
STUDY GUIDE

● Population Impact on the Environment

Cross out the statements that are NOT correct.

1. A population is the total number of individuals of a particular species in a particular area.

2. Earth's population is decreasing.

3. *Population explosion* is a term that is used to describe the rapid rate at which people are reproducing.

4. Each day, more than 260 000 people are added to Earth's population.

5. In the 1800s, the world population reached about a billion.

6. During the last two centuries, the rate of population increase has slowed.

7. The number of people on Earth does not affect the environment.

8. In the past, Earth didn't have resources to support the population.

9. The average person in the United States uses less energy than the average person in the rest of the world.

10. Electricity is generated by burning fuels.

11. Plastic products affect the environment.

12. Removing Earth's resources doesn't affect the land.

13. Shaping resources into usable products affects the environment.

14. Farming prevents topsoil from being lost.

15. Much of the food you eat is grown using chemicals in the process.

16. The population is predicted to be 14 billion sometime in the next century.

17. Modern medicine, better sanitation, and better nutrition have all helped to slow the death rate.

Chapter 19

STUDY GUIDE

● Using the Land

Determine whether each of the following statements is true or false. Write the word "true" or "false" in the blank. Then in the space below the statements, tell why each false statement is false.

_____ 1. Most of the land on Earth is farmland.

_____ 2. Since 1985, the problem of world hunger has been solved.

_____ 3. Eroded topsoil can be replaced within a year.

_____ 4. Herbicides and pesticides, often used on crops, may contaminate waterways.

_____ 5. Destruction of trees causes other plants and animals to die.

_____ 6. In a sanitary landfill, each day's deposit of garbage is covered with dirt.

_____ 7. Hazardous waste may be poisonous or radioactive.

_____ 8. Batteries and medicine are two kinds of hazardous waste.

_____ 9. Many cities put trash and garbage in landfills.

_____ 10. Paving the land is one way to protect the environment.

_____ 11. Conservation is a careful use of resources.

_____ 12. Conservation eliminates all damage to the environment.

_____ 13. Piling up cut grass and leaves so they can decompose is called composting.

_____

_____

_____

_____

_____

_____

_____

_____

_____

_____

Chapter 19

STUDY GUIDE

Text Pages 546–548

• Should Recycling Be Required?

Use the words in the box to fill in the blanks.

garbage	require	energy	trees
natural resources	60	cheaper	
recyclable	40	mass	

1. An object is _____ if it can be processed and used again.

2. If you recycle, you will reduce the trash you generate in your lifetime by _____ percent.

3. Recycling saves landfill space, energy, and _____ resources.

4. If you don't recycle, you will generate trash equal to at least 600 times your _____ .

5. In some places, _____ is not collected if it contains items that should have been recycled.

6. One problem for recycling paper is that new paper is _____ than recycled paper.

7. Paper makes up about _____ percent of the mass of our trash.

8. If you recycle paper, you help reduce the damage caused by cutting _____ .

9. Recycling one aluminum can saves enough _____ to keep a TV running for three hours.

10. Many state and city governments promote recycling. Some of them _____ recycling.

Answer the following questions on the lines provided.

11. How are trash-collection fees used in some places to promote recycling? _____
_____

12. What are some of the economic costs of recycling? _____
_____

Chapter 20

STUDY GUIDE

• Air Pollution

Match the items in Column I with the phrases in Column II. Write the letter of the correct phrase in the blank at the left.

Column I

_____ **1.** acid rain

_____ **2.** acid

_____ **3.** base

_____ **4.** carbon monoxide

_____ **5.** 1990 Clean Air Act

_____ **6.** mountains and valleys

_____ **7.** natural sources of pollution

_____ **8.** photochemical smog

_____ **9.** pH scale

_____ **10.** sulfurous smog

Column II

a. Colorless, odorless gas present in some smog

b. Occurs when nitrogen compounds react with sunlight

c. Volcanic eruptions, forest fires, and grass fires

d. Landforms that help smog form

e. Sulfur dioxide or nitrogen compounds combined with moisture in the air

f. Goals to clean up the air in the United States

g. Formed when fossil fuels are burned, releasing sulfur compounds, dust, and smoke particles where there is little wind

h. Type of solution with a low pH number

i. Measure of acidity in a solution

j. Type of solution with a high pH number

Finish the puzzle below. Then unscramble the letters in the boxes to complete Item 15.

11. smoke + fog = ___ ☐ ___ ___

12. nitrogen + oxygen =

☐ ☐ ___ ___ ☐ ___ ___ ___   ___ ___ ___ ☐ ☐ ___ ☐ ___

13. sulfur compounds + stagnant air =

___ ☐ ☐ ___ ___ ☐ ___ ___ ___   ___ ___ ☐ ___

14. pollutants + sunlight =

___ ___ ___ ☐ ___ ___ ___ ☐ ___ ___ ___ ___ ☐ ___   ___ ___ ☐ ___

15. Goal of the 1990 Clean Air Act =

___ ___   ___ ___ ___ ___   ___ ___ ___ ___ ___ ___ ___ ___

Chapter 20

STUDY GUIDE

• Acid Rain

Use the words in the boxes to fill in the blanks.

acidic	factories	soil
basic	nitrogen gases	wind
cars	Midwest	sulfur

The amount of acid rain in an area depends on the number of _____ and

_____ in the area. This is because they are the sources of

_____ and _____ that become acid rain.

Does acid rain fall where the pollution starts? It depends on the _____ ,

which sometimes carries the pollution away.

When acid rain does fall, the damage it does depends partly on the kind of

_____ in the area. Some soils are already _____ ,

and plants that grow in them can't survive when more acid is added. Other soils are

_____ , and the damage is less when acid rain falls on these. As a rule, soils

in the _____ are basic and soils in the northeastern states are acidic.

sulfur	coal-burning	jobs
car exhaust	public transportation	car pooling
cost	scrubber	coal
nitric acid		

Acid rain is created when moisture in the air combines with nitrogen oxide to form

_____ . Do you know what the main source of nitrogen oxide is? It comes

from _____ . Two ways people can help to reduce nitric acid are by

_____ and using _____ .

Another source of acid rain comes from _____ power plants that release

_____ into the air. Power plants can help this situation in two ways. They

can wash the _____ , and they can run the smoke through a

_____ .

Why don't people insist that power plants make their exhaust cleaner? Because the

_____ of electricity would increase and because many people could lose their

_____ .

Chapter 20

STUDY GUIDE

• Water Pollution

A word has been scrambled in each of the following statements. Unscramble the word and write it on the line provided.

_____ 1. Tests of rivers, streams, and lakes show that some have been polluted by **beairact** from raw sewage.

_____ 2. Dumping raw sewage is an **aglille** act.

_____ 3. Barrels of waste from nuclear power plants may leak materials that are **taciodivera.**

_____ 4. Water running through mines carries pollutants to underground **quaierfs.**

_____ 5. Water is polluted every time you **shaw.**

_____ 6. Sometimes countries work together to **drecue** pollution.

_____ 7. In the 1970s, Canada and the United States made two water **lautiqy** agreements.

_____ 8. **zhousdara** wastes poured directly onto the ground may move through the soil.

_____ 9. If you have a question about how to get rid of hazardous wastes, call your garbage **plaidoss** service for information.

_____ 10. A way for individuals to reduce water pollution is to conserve **neegry.**

Complete the chart by listing each of the following sentences under the correct heading.

- The United States passed it in 1986.
- The United States passed it in 1987.
- It ensures that drinking water is safe.
- It gives money to states to build sewage plants.

- It gives money to states to build wastewater treatment facilities.
- It requires states to develop water quality standards for all streams.
- Some cities still do not meet its standards.

Safe Drinking Water Act	Clean Water Act
1.	1.
2.	2.
3.	3.
	4.

Chapter 21

STUDY GUIDE

Text Pages 584–590

● Radiation from Space

Decide if each statement is true or false. If false, change the italicized word or words to make the statement correct and write your answer in the blank at the left. If the statement is correct, write true in the blank.

_____ 1. Unlike mechanical waves, electromagnetic waves can travel through *matter*.

_____ 2. *Radiation* is energy that's transmitted from one place to another by electromagnetic waves.

_____ 3. A *refracting* telescope uses mirrors to focus light from the object being viewed.

_____ 4. In a vacuum, the *speed of light* equals 300 000 km/s.

_____ 5. Unlike visible light, radio waves *can't pass* freely through Earth's atmosphere.

_____ 6. Today, *optical telescopes* the size of three football fields are being used.

_____ 7. The *Hubble Space Telescope* is an example of an optical telescope.

_____ 8. Sound waves are examples of *mechanical* waves.

_____ 9. Radio telescopes are used to study *visible light* waves.

_____ 10. Types of electromagnetic waves differ in their *speeds*.

_____ 11. Most optical telescopes used by professional astronomers are in *observatories*.

_____ 12. For us to hear astronauts' voices from space, the sound waves must be converted into *gamma rays* and then converted back to sound waves.

_____ 13. Different types of magnetic waves travel at *different* speeds.

_____ 14. Earth's *atmosphere* absorbs and distorts some of the energy we receive from space objects.

_____ 15. The arrangement of the types of radiant energy according to their wavelengths is called the *electromagnetic spectrum*.

_____ 16. Both reflecting and refracting telescopes are *optical* telescopes.

_____ 17. *Magnetic* waves travel at the speed of light.

Chapter 21

STUDY GUIDE   • Light Pollution

Each number in the code below represents a letter. Use the code to decode the message. After you've decoded the message, answer the question.

Code:

1	2	3	4	5	6	7	8	9	10	11	12	13	14	15	16	17	18	19	20	21	22	23	24	25	26
A	C	E	G	I	K	M	O	Q	S	U	W	Y	B	D	F	H	J	L	N	P	R	T	V	X	Z

23 17 3   10 23 1 22 10   8 16   23 17 3

__ __ __   __ __ __ __ __   __ __   __ __ __

20 5 4 17 23   10 6 13   2 1 20' 23   14 3

__ __ __ __ __   __ __ __   __ __ __ __   __ __

10 3 3 20   16 22 8 7   17 3 22 3

__ __ __ __   __ __ __ __   __ __ __ __

23 17 3   14 22 5 4 17 23   2 5 23 13

__ __ __   __ __ __ __ __ __   __ __ __ __

19 5 4 17 23 10   1 22 3   8 11 10 23   23 8 8

__ __ __ __ __ __   __ __ __   __ __ __ __   __ __ __

19 3 1 22

__ __ __ __

23 17 3 13   2 1 11 10 3   1   4 19 8 12

__ __ __ __   __ __ __ __ __   __   __ __ __ __

2 1 19 19 3 15   19 5 4 17 23

__ __ __ __ __ __   __ __ __ __ __

21 8 19 19 11 23 5 8 20   16 8 22   12 17 5 2 17

__ __ __ __ __ __ __ __ __   __ __ __   __ __ __ __ __

12 3   17 1 24 3   20 8   3 1 10 13

__ __   __ __ __ __   __ __   __ __ __ __

10 8 19 11 23 5 8 20

__ __ __ __ __ __ __ __

Name two things that can be done to reduce light pollution. _____

_____

_____

Chapter 21
STUDY GUIDE

Text Pages 594–603

● Artificial Satellites and Space Probes

Study the illustration. Identify A and B in the illustration and write the correct term in the space provided. Then under each spacecraft's name, write the number of each item below that describes it. If an item describes both, write the number under both names.

A. _____

_____

_____

_____

_____

B. _____

_____

_____

_____

_____

_____

1. This is any object that revolves around another object.

2. *Voyager 1* and *Voyager 2* are examples of this.

3. John Glenn was the first citizen of the United States to orbit Earth in one of these.

4. The moon is an example of one of these.

5. *Sputnik 1* was the first spacecraft of this type.

6. This spacecraft travels far into the solar system, collecting and transmitting data to Earth.

7. The spacecraft *Galileo* is one of these.

8. These transmit information to Earth.

9. Its path is called an orbit.

Match the project in Column I with its description in Column II.

Column I

_____ 10. Project *Apollo*

_____ 11. Project *Mercury*

_____ 12. Project *Gemini*

Column II

a. First program in the race for space. Goals were to orbit an astronaut in a spacecraft around Earth and bring him down safely.

b. Second program in the race for space. Goal was for one spacecraft to connect with another while in orbit.

c. Third program in the race for space. Goal was for astronauts to land on the moon.

Chapter 21
STUDY GUIDE

• The Space Shuttle and the Future

Read the following statements. If a statement is true of a space shuttle, write SH in the blank. If a statement is true of a space station, write ST. If the statement is true of both, write B in the blank.

_____ 1. The United States has developed this type of spacecraft.

_____ 2. This is a reusable space transport.

_____ 3. Its solid-fuel booster engines are recovered after they are parachuted to Earth.

_____ 4. This has orbited Earth.

_____ 5. Cosmonauts spent a record 365 days in one of these.

_____ 6. NASA plans on assembling a future one of these in orbit.

_____ 7. This provides living quarters for work and exercise for people living in space.

_____ 8. Astronauts have conducted experiments in these.

_____ 9. This glides back to Earth and lands like an airplane.

_____ 10. NASA plans call for crews to remain on board this several months at a time.

_____ 11. This would be used in the future to send equipment and goods back and forth to people working in space.

_____ 12. Its mechanical arm can be used to launch, retrieve, and repair satellites.

_____ 13. The Soviets called theirs *Mir*.

_____ 14. We called ours *Skylab*.

_____ 15. The *Hubble Space Telescope* was launched by this in 1990.

_____ 16. A purpose of this is to serve as a repair site for satellites and other vehicles.

_____ 17. Its liquid-fuel tank is not recovered when it returns to Earth.

_____ 18. Astronauts can only spend a short time in space in one of these.

_____ 19. In one of these, American crews have spent up to 84 days collecting data about the effects of living in space.

_____ 20. NASA has plans for the future use of this.

_____ 21. Astronauts on this perform many duties.

_____ 22. Several nations will cooperate in working on a future project for this.

_____ 23. While in this, researchers will make products that will be returned to Earth.

Chapter 22
STUDY GUIDE

● Planet Earth

Use the words in the box to fill in the blanks in the statements.

revolution	ellipse	seasons
sphere-shaped	sphere	center
24 hours	365 days	rotation
axis		

1. A round, three dimensional object is a _____ .

2. All points on a sphere's surface are the same distance from the _____ of the sphere.

3. Images from space probes and artificial satellites show that Earth is _____ .

4. The North and South Poles are located at the ends of Earth's _____ , the imaginary line around which Earth spins.

5. The spinning of Earth on its axis that causes day and night is called _____ .

6. One complete rotation of Earth takes about _____ .

7. Earth's yearly orbit around the sun is its _____ .

8. One complete revolution of Earth takes about _____ .

9. The path of Earth's orbit is in the shape of an elongated closed curve called an

   _____ .

10. Earth's tilted axis causes _____ .

Answer the following questions on the lines provided.

11. What is inclined at an angle of 11.5° to Earth's rotational axis? _____

12. What is the sun directly over at the equinoxes? _____

13. Which season begins in the northern hemisphere when the sun reaches its greatest distance south

    of the equator? _____

14. On what date does the southern hemisphere begin spring? _____

15. At the March equinox, what season begins in the northern hemisphere? _____

16. At the summer solstice in the northern hemisphere, at what point is the sun?

    _____

Chapter 22
STUDY GUIDE

● Earth's Moon

In the blank at the left, write the term from the box that matches the description.

lunar eclipse	first quarter	full moon	waning gibbous
new moon	solar eclipse	maria	third quarter
waxing	waxing gibbous	waning	waning crescent
moon phases			

_____ 1. Changing appearances of the moons as seen from Earth

_____ 2. Phase of the moon when you see only half of the lighted side after a full moon

_____ 3. Period when the amount of the lighted side that can be seen becomes increasingly smaller

_____ 4. Phase that starts just after the full moon

_____ 5. Period after a new moon when more and more of the lighted side of the moon becomes visible

_____ 6. Phase when the lighted half of the moon is facing the sun and the dark side faces Earth

_____ 7. Waxing phase of the moon when you can see half of the lighted side, or one-quarter, of the moon's surface

_____ 8. Phase of the moon when the half of the moon's surface facing Earth is lighted

_____ 9. Waxing period when more than one-quarter but less than half of the lighted side of the moon's surface can be seen

_____ 10. Occurs when the moon moves directly between the sun and Earth and casts a shadow on part of Earth

_____ 11. Occurs when Earth's shadow falls on the moon

_____ 12. Dark-colored, relatively flat regions of lava on the moon's surface

_____ 13. Occurs just before a new moon

Write an F next to the statements that are false.

_____ 14. The moon rotates on its axis once every 365 days.

_____ 15. The moon completes one revolution around Earth every 27.3 days.

_____ 16. The large depressions on the moon that are caused by meteorites are called crescents.

_____ 17. One half of the moon is always lighted because it faces the sun.

_____ 18. At full moon, we see 100 percent of the moon.

Chapter 22

STUDY GUIDE

• Exploration of the Moon

Circle the word in parentheses that makes each statement correct.

1. *Clementine* orbited the moon for two (months, years).

2. *Clementine* took high-resolution (photographs, sonographs).

3. *Clementine* could detect something that was only (2, 200) meters across.

4. The South Pole-Aitken Basin is the (oldest, youngest) identifiable impact feature on the moon.

5. Much of the South Pole-Aitken Basin is in (shadow, sunlight).

6. *Clementine* found out that the moon's crust (thickens, thins) under impact basins.

7. *Clementine* studied (stars, moon rocks) as part of its mission.

8. It was decided that *Clementine* was a (failure, success).

Put an X by the sentences that are true about moon exploration.

ــــــــ 9. *Clementine* collected data necessary for astronauts to walk on the moon.

ــــــــ 10. *Clementine* tested new sensors for tracking cold objects in space.

ــــــــ 11. An example of a cold object is a satellite.

ــــــــ 12. *Clementine* got its name from these sensors.

ــــــــ 13. *Clementine* studied the sun as well as the moon.

ــــــــ 14. The South Pole-Aitken Basin is the largest depression found in the solar system.

ــــــــ 15. *Clementine* photographed the South Pole-Aitken Basin.

ــــــــ 16. Ice may be found in the South Pole-Aitken Basin.

ــــــــ 17. If water were found in the South Pole-Aitken Basin, a moon colony there would be in danger from floods.

ــــــــ 18. Any type of moon colony would probably be powered by energy from water.

ــــــــ 19. *Clementine* discovered that the moon's crust on the side facing Earth is much thinner than the crust on the far side.

ــــــــ 20. *Clementine*'s map showed mascons, which are concentrations of mass.

ــــــــ 21. *Clementine* found out information about minerals on the moon.

ــــــــ 22. Humans are scheduled to walk on the moon again in 1999.

• The Solar System

Write the term or phrase that matches each definition in the spaces provided. The letters in the boxes make a word that answers Question 10 below.

1. ＿ ＿ ＿ ＿ ＿ ＿ ＿ ＿ ☐ ＿

2. ＿ ＿ ＿ ＿ ＿ ＿ ＿ ＿ ☐ ＿

3. ＿ ＿ ＿ ☐ ＿

4. ＿ ＿ ＿ ☐

5. ＿ ＿ ＿ ☐

6. ＿ ＿ ☐

7. ☐ ＿ ＿ ＿ ＿

8. ＿ ＿ ＿ ＿ ＿   ＿ ＿ ＿ ＿ ☐

9. ☐ ＿ ＿ ＿ ＿ ＿ ＿ ＿

1. Shape of the planets' orbits, discovered by Kepler

2. Polish astronomer who proposed a different model of the solar system

3. Placed at the center of the Greeks' model of the solar system

4. Planets closest to the sun—Mercury, Venus, Earth, Mars

5. Process involved in the forming of the sun

6. Placed at the center of the Polish astronomer's model of the solar system

7. Planets farthest from the sun—Jupiter, Saturn, Uranus, Neptune, Pluto

8. Made up of the sun and all the objects that orbit it

9. Light element found in most of the outer planets

10. What is the study of the universe called? ＿ ＿ ＿ ＿ ＿ ＿ ＿ ＿ ＿

Chapter 23

STUDY GUIDE

Text Pages 646–651

● The Inner Planets

In the blank at the left, write the letter of the term or phrase that correctly completes each statement.

_____ 1. Mars is the _____ planet outward from the sun.
    a. third   **b.** fourth

_____ 2. Because of similar size and mass, _____ is called Earth's twin.
    a. Mars   **b.** Venus

_____ 3. _____ has great extremes in temperature, –450°C during the day and –170°C at night.
    a. Mercury   **b.** Mars

_____ 4. Venus is the _____ planet outward from the sun.
    a. fourth   **b.** second

_____ 5. The _____ space probes made many discoveries about Mars.
    a. *Viking*   **b.** *Mariner*

_____ 6. The atmosphere of _____ is mostly carbon dioxide.
    a. Mercury   **b.** Venus

_____ 7. The largest volcano in the solar system is _____ on Mars.
    a. *Valles Marineras*   **b.** *Olympus Mons*

_____ 8. One astronomical unit (AU) is equal to the avenge distance between the sun and _____.
    a. Earth   **b.** Mercury

_____ 9. One astronomical until (AU) equals _____.
    a. 150 million km   **b.** 15 million km

_____ 10. Water exists as a solid, liquid, and gas on _____.
    a. Mercury   **b.** Earth

_____ 11. Polar ice caps are a visible feature of _____.
    a. Mars   **b.** Venus

_____ 12. Mars appears red because of _____ in its rocks.
    a. sulfuric acid   **b.** iron oxide

_____ 13. _____ is the third planet outward from the sun.
    a. Venus   **b.** Earth

_____ 14. _____ is the larger of Mars' two moons.
    a. Phobos   **b.** Deimos

_____ 15. The _____ space probe mapped the surface of Venus.
    a. *Magellan*   **b.** *Mariner*

Chapter 23
STUDY GUIDE

● Mission to Mars

Determine whether each of the following statements is true or false. Write the word "true" or "false" in the blank. If the statement is false, rewrite it so that it's true.

_____ 1. Only humans can carry out scientific experiments on Mars.

_____

_____

_____ 2. The near zero gravity in space can cause human bones to lose calcium, weaken, and break more easily.

_____

_____ 3. Human muscles are not affected by the lack of gravity in space.

_____

_____

_____ 4. It would take about three months to get to Mars and back.

_____

_____ 5. A robot's hands can be controlled by sensors connected to data gloves worn by a human operator.

_____

_____ 6. A robot "sees" with tiny video cameras.

_____

_____ 7. Radio signals travel from Earth to Mars in a few seconds.

_____

_____ 8. Scientists have already developed robots with sufficient artificial intelligence to work on Mars.

_____

_____

_____ 9. Because of the long flight to Mars, humans would face more danger than they do on current missions.

_____

_____ 10. Body fluids move upward because there's no gravity to pull them down.

_____

STUDY GUIDE   ● **The Outer Planets**

Decide if a statement is true or false. If false, change the italicized word or words to make the statement correct and write your answer in the blank. If the statement is correct, write "true" in the blank.

_____ 1. Ganymede, the largest satellite in the solar system, is one of *Neptune's* 16 moons.

_____ 2. All of the outer planets except Pluto are large and *gaseous*.

_____ 3. *Neptune* is the only planet that rotates on an axis parallel to its orbit.

_____ 4. The largest of Saturn's moons, *Charon*, is larger than Mercury.

_____ 5. *Io* is volcanically active because of Jupiter's gravitational force.

_____ 6. *Saturn* is the largest planet and the fifth planet outward from the sun.

_____ 7. Much of the information about the outer planets was discovered by the *Viking* space probes.

_____ 8. Unlike the other outer planets, *Pluto* has a solid, rocky surface.

_____ 9. Uranus is the *sixth* planet outward from the sun.

_____ 10. A large swirling storm on Jupiter is called the *Titan*.

_____ 11. Pluto is not always *closest to* the sun because its orbit crosses Neptune's orbit.

_____ 12. *Charon* and Pluto are sometimes called a double planet.

_____ 13. *Saturn* is known for its rings and its very low density.

_____ 14. The blue-green color of Uranus and Neptune is caused by *carbon dioxide* in their atmospheres.

_____ 15. *Neptune* is usually the eighth planet outward from the sun.

• Other Objects in the Solar System

Text Pages 662–669

Solve the crossword puzzle by using the definitions provided as clues.

Across

3. Composed of dust, rock particles, and frozen water and gases

4. Cloud of vaporized gases around a comet's nucleus

7. Name of cloud that contains many comets outside of the solar system

8. Small pieces of rock from broken-up comets moving through space

9. Meteoroid that burns up in Earth's atmosphere

11. Largest asteroid in the asteroid belt

Down

1. Meteoroid that strikes Earth

2. Area between Mars and Jupiter where many asteroids are located

5. Piece of rock similar to material that formed into planets

6. Group of meteors

10. Part of comet that always points away from the sun

Chapter 24

STUDY GUIDE

● Stars

Decide if each statement below is true or false. If false, change the italicized word or words to make the statement correct and write your answer in the blank at the left. If the statement is correct, write "true" in the blank.

_____ 1. A group of stars that form a pattern is called a *constellation*.

_____ 2. The amount of light that Earth receives from a star is called the star's *absolute magnitude*.

_____ 3. The distances of stars from Earth are measured in *parallaxes*.

_____ 4. Very hot stars are a *blue-white* color.

_____ 5. The *apparent magnitude* of a star is the amount of light it actually gives off.

_____ 6. Another name for the North Star is *Polaris*.

_____ 7. The absolute magnitude of Rigel is *less than* that of Sirius.

_____ 8. The apparent shift in an object when viewed from two different positions is called *parallax*.

_____ 9. The pattern of dark lines recorded by a spectrograph can be used to identify the *elements* that are in a star's atmosphere.

_____ 10. The stars appear to change positions in the sky throughout the year because *Earth revolves around the sun*.

_____ 11. A light-year is the *speed* that light travels in one year.

_____ 12. The apparent magnitude of stars is *greater* when they are closer to Earth.

_____ 13. Constellations that circle Polaris and are visible year-round are called *circumpolar* constellations.

_____ 14. The star *Betelgeuse* is almost directly over Earth's north pole.

_____ 15. All of the constellations appear to be moving because *Earth* is moving.

Chapter 24

STUDY GUIDE

● **The Sun**

Identify the sun's features in the illustration by writing the name of each feature in the appropriate space below. The features are listed in the box.

core	corona	solar wind	chromosphere
photosphere	solar flares	prominence	sunspot

1. _____

2. _____

3. _____

4. _____

5. _____

6. _____

7. _____

8. _____

In the space provided, fill in the missing term. Choose terms from the box above.

_____ 1. In the _____ , hydrogen is fused into helium.

_____ 2. A _____ is a dark area of the sun that is cooler than the surrounding area.

_____ 3. The _____ is the lowest layer of the sun's atmosphere from which light is given off.

_____ 4. _____ is made up of charged particles that continually escape from the corona and move through space

_____ 5. The _____ is the largest layer of the sun's atmosphere.

_____ 6. The _____ extends upward about 10 000 km.

_____ 7. A huge, arching column of gas is a _____ .

_____ 8. Gases near a sunspot that suddenly brighten, shooting gas outward at high speed, are called _____ .

Chapter 24

STUDY GUIDE

● Evolution of Stars

Use the diagram to help you complete the following statements by circling the most appropriate term in the parentheses.

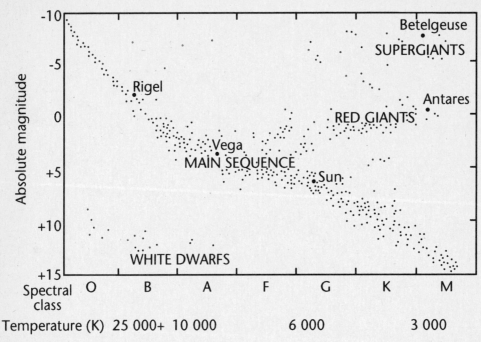

1. White dwarfs are very hot stars that have (high, low) absolute magnitudes.

2. Main sequence stars are stars that fit into a (diagonal, vertical) band that run from the upper left to the lower right on the diagram.

3. Although its temperature is greater, our sun has lower absolute magnitude than that of (Betelgeuse, Vega).

4. On the diagram, our sun is identified as having an absolute magnitude of about (–5, +5).

5. Supergiants are stars with relatively (high, low) temperatures and high absolute magnitudes.

6. Red giants (are, are not) main sequence stars.

7. The absolute magnitude of Rigel is (higher, lower) than that of the sun.

8. The temperature of Rigel is (higher, lower) than that of the sun.

9. Betelgeuse is (hotter, colder) than Rigel.

10. Betelgeuse has an absolute magnitude that is (greater, less) than that of Rigel.

11. A star that lies outside the main sequence is (Rigel, Antares).

12. White dwarfs and red giants lie (outside, inside) the main sequence.

Chapter 24

STUDY GUIDE

• Galaxies and the Expanding Universe

Text Pages 691–697

Write the term that matches each description in the spaces provided. Place one letter in each space. One letter has been given for each answer.

1. __ __ __ __ __   __ [A] __

2. __ __ __ __ __ __ [S] __

3. __ __ __ __ __ [G] __ __ __ __

4. __ __ __   __ [A] __ __   __ __ __ __ __ __

5. __ __ __ __ __ __ __ __   __ __ __ __ [X] __ __ __

6. __ __ __ [E] __ __ __ __ __ __

7. __ __ [I] __ __ __ __ __

8. __ __ __ __ [L] __ __   __ __ __ __ __

1. This is the name of the galaxy in which you live.

2. Scientists determined this was expanding by using the spectrograph.

3. This cluster of galaxies is made up of about twenty-five galaxies including the Milky Way.

4. According to this theory, billions of years ago the universe began expanding out of an enormous explosion.

5. This class of galaxies includes football-shaped galaxies.

6. These galaxies are usually small and have many different shapes.

7. These galaxies have arms winding outward from inner regions.

8. This is the change of color on the spectrograph as objects move toward or away from other objects.

Write the clue letters that were given in the answers: _____

Rearrange the letters to form a word for the groups of stars, dust, and gas held together by gravity.

_____

Chapter 24
STUDY GUIDE

Text Pages 698–703

• The Search for Extraterrestrial Life

Match the description in Column I with the correct terms in Column II. Write the letter of the correct terms in the space provided.

Column I

_____ 1. Program that searches for extraterrestrial life

_____ 2. Showed no evidence of the kind of molecules that seem necessary for life

_____ 3. Life that exists beyond Earth

_____ 4. A satellite of Neptune that contains molecules that resemble those from which life on Earth probably evolved

_____ 5. A moon of Jupiter that may possibly receive sunlight on its ocean

_____ 6. Sterilized so it wouldn't contaminate soil on Mars

_____ 7. Sent a probe into Jupiter's clouds

_____ 8. Molecules from which life evolved

Column II

a. Triton

b. extraterrestrial life

c. Martian soil

d. SETI

e. *Viking*

f. organic molecules

g. Europa

h. *Galileo*

Unscramble the following words to reveal what SETI stands for.

eth   _____

chears   _____

orf   _____

xtttrrrreeeaails   _____

elligtennice   _____

Chapter 1
STUDY GUIDE

Applying Science

Text Pages 10–11

Unscramble the scrambled words. Put your answers in the blanks provided to complete the paragraph. Then answer the questions.

Technology is the use of enifitsicc **scientific** _____ discoveries. Technology has enabled people to clear sterofs **forests** _____ and build cities. It's led to the development of modern camshine **machines** _____ such as cars and computers. Because of technology, work that is dangerous for people to do can now be done by stoobr **robots** _____ . People can now live longer because cloghoteny **technology** _____ has improved medicines, health care, and foods. Technology is responsible for many improvements, but it has also created brompels **problems** _____ . Some uses of technology cause loptulnoi **pollution** _____ . For example, air conditioners can keep rooms cool, but they also release a chemical that can harm the montinvener **environment** _____ .

1. What is the topic of the paragraph? **technology** _____

2. What is technology? **Technology is the use of scientific discoveries.** _____

3. Name the machines identified in the paragraph. **cars, computers, robots, and air conditioners** _____

4. Why are robots useful to people? **Robots can do work that is dangerous for people to do.** _____

5. How has technology helped people live longer? **Through technology, medicine, health care, and foods have been improved so that people now live longer than they used to live.** _____

6. Does technology cause any problems? Explain. **Yes, technology can cause problems such as pollution.** _____

7. How are air conditioners helpful to people? **Air conditioners can keep rooms cool.** _____

8. How can air conditioners be harmful? **Air conditioners can release a chemical harmful to the environment.** _____

5

Chapter 1
STUDY GUIDE

What Is Earth Science?

Text Pages 6–9

Use the terms in the box to complete the sentences.

science	physics	astronomy
chemistry	Earth science	meteorology
life science	geology	oceanography

Science 1. _____ is a process of observing and studying things in our world.

Earth science 2. The four major sciences include _____, life science, chemistry, and physics.

Life science 3. _____ is the science that studies living organisms.

astronomy 4. The science of _____ is the study of objects in space.

physics 5. When you study forces, motion, energy, and their effects on matter, you are studying _____.

geology 6. In _____, scientists study Earth, its matter, and the processes that form and change Earth.

Chemistry 7. _____ is the study of the properties and composition of matter.

meteorology 8. The study of weather and the forces and processes that cause it is called _____.

oceanography 9. In _____, people study the processes that occur within the ocean and the effects humans have on these processes.

Complete Items 10 and 11 on the lines provided.

10. List four specific areas of study of Earth science.
   geology _____
   meteorology _____
   astronomy _____
   oceanography _____

11. Use Table 1-1 in your text. What will you study in Earth science? **planet Earth and its place in space** _____

Chapter 1
STUDY GUIDE

Text Pages 12–18

● Solving Problems

In the blank, write the letter of the term or phrase that best completes each statement.

__b__ 1. The first step in any problem-solving strategy is to _____.
a. collect information about the problem   b. identify the problem

__b__ 2. The method used by scientists for solving problems is known as the _____.
a. control   b. scientific method

__a__ 3. A prediction about a problem that can be tested is a _____.
a. hypothesis   b. conclusion

__b__ 4. A _____ is a standard for comparison in an experiment.
a. variable   b. control

__a__ 5. An explanation backed by results obtained from repeated tests or experiments is a _____.
a. theory   b. variable

__b__ 6. A process that uses certain skills to solve problems is called _____.
a. theory   b. critical thinking

__a__ 7. A _____ is a changeable factor in an experiment.
a. variable   b. control

__a__ 8. The best experiments test only one _____ at a time.
a. variable   b. control

__b__ 9. If a conclusion does not support a hypothesis, the _____.
a. experiment did not work properly   b. hypothesis should be revised

__b__ 10. If a hypothesis is supported by new data gathered over a period of time, it may become a _____.
a. control   b. theory

__a__ 11. Making lists, drawing graphs, making a model, and eliminating possibilities are all for solving problems.
a. strategies   b. variables

__b__ 12. If a hypothesis has been backed by results from repeated tests or experiments, it becomes a _____.
a. variable   b. theory

Chapter 1
STUDY GUIDE

Text Pages 19–29

● Measurement and Safety

Find the words or prefixes in the puzzle that match the definitions below. Circle the words in the puzzle. Then write each word next to its definition.

mass _____ 1. Measure of the amount of matter in an object

Celsius _____ 2. Temperature measurement in which freezing is 0° and boiling is 100°

area _____ 3. Amount of surface within a set of boundaries

centi _____ 4. Prefix meaning one hundredth

gravity _____ 5. Force that pulls particles of matter toward other particles of matter

meter _____ 6. Standard unit in SI of length

density _____ 7. Measure of the amount of matter that occupies a space

Kelvin _____ 8. Standard unit in SI for temperature

weight _____ 9. Measure of the force of gravity that is expressed in newtons

gram _____ 10. Standard unit in SI of measure for mass

volume _____ 11. Measure of how much space an object occupies

milli _____ 12. Prefix meaning one thousandth

SI _____ 13. What two letters were not circled in the puzzle?

Answer the questions on the lines provided.

14. What are the two letters SI an abbreviation for? __International System of Units__

15. Why must safe practices and methods be used in laboratory activities? __to help protect people from injury from equipment or chemicals__

Chapter 2
STUDY GUIDE

Combinations of Atoms

Use the words in the box to complete the statements. You will use the words more than once.

molecule	compound	chemical properties	ions	mixture

1. The components of a **mixture** can be separated by physical means.

2. The **chemical properties** of an element determine how the element will change when it reacts with another element.

3. A **compound** is a substance that has different properties from the elements in it.

4. Combined atoms form a **molecule**.

5. Electrically charged atoms are **ions**.

6. Table salt is an example of a **compound**.

7. An example of a **mixture** is salt water.

8. Table salt is formed when the **ions** of sodium and chlorine combine.

9. Iron rusts when it comes in contact with water because of its **chemical properties**.

10. The atoms of hydrogen and oxygen combine to form a **molecule** of the compound water.

Identify the two atoms that are ions. Label the negatively charged ion with a minus sign. Label the positively charged ion with a plus sign.

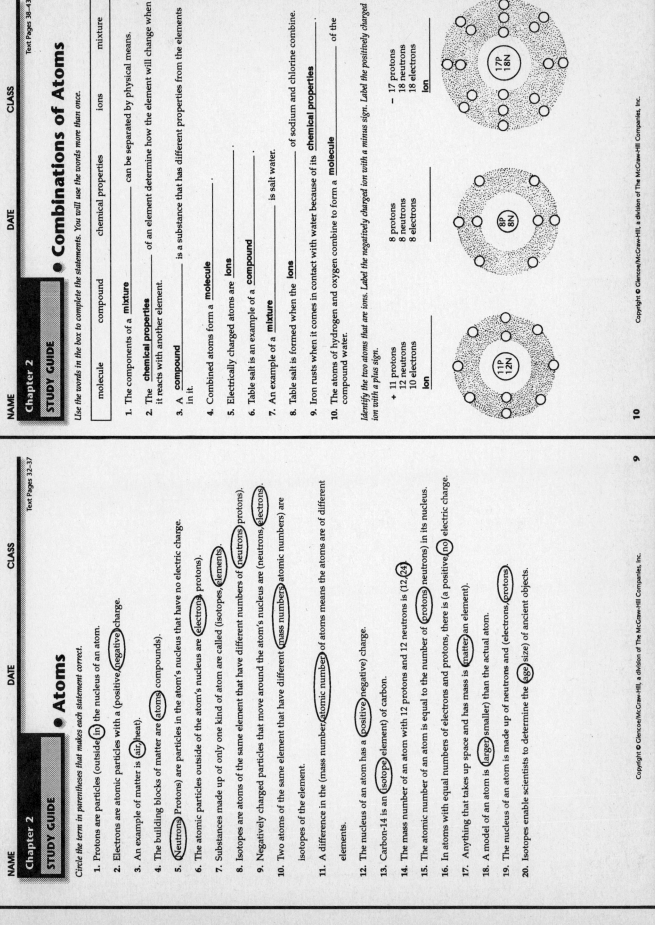

11P 12N — + 11 protons, 12 neutrons, 10 electrons — Ion

8P 8N — 8 protons, 8 neutrons, 8 electrons

17P 18N — − 17 protons, 18 neutrons, 18 electrons — Ion

Chapter 2
STUDY GUIDE

Atoms

Circle the term in parentheses that makes each statement correct.

1. Protons are particles (outside, **in**) the nucleus of an atom.

2. Electrons are atomic particles with a (positive, **negative**) charge.

3. An example of matter is (**air**, heat).

4. The building blocks of matter are (**atoms**, compounds).

5. (**Neutrons**, Protons) are particles in the atom's nucleus that have no electric charge.

6. The atomic particles outside of the atom's nucleus are (**electrons**, protons).

7. Substances made up of only one kind of atom are called (isotopes, **elements**).

8. Isotopes are atoms of the same element that have different numbers of (**neutrons**, protons).

9. Negatively charged particles that move around the atom's nucleus are (neutrons, **electrons**).

10. Two atoms of the same element that have different (**mass numbers**, atomic numbers) are isotopes of the element.

11. A difference in the (mass number, **atomic number**) of atoms means the atoms are of different elements.

12. The nucleus of an atom has a (**positive**, negative) charge.

13. Carbon-14 is an (**isotope**, element) of carbon.

14. The mass number of an atom with 12 protons and 12 neutrons is (12, **24**).

15. The atomic number of an atom is equal to the number of (**protons**, neutrons) in its nucleus.

16. In atoms with equal numbers of electrons and protons, there is (a positive, **no**) electric charge.

17. Anything that takes up space and has mass is (**matter**, an element).

18. A model of an atom is (**larger**, smaller) than the actual atom.

19. The nucleus of an atom is made up of neutrons and (electrons, **protons**).

20. Isotopes enable scientists to determine the (**age**, size) of ancient objects.

Chapter 2

STUDY GUIDE ● **Matter**

Change the italicized word in each statement to make the statement correct.

1. The *size* of an object determines whether it will float in water. __The density of an object determines whether it will float in water.__

2. Orange juice and milk are both *solids*. __Orange juice and milk are both liquids.__

3. Stars are made up of matter in the *gaseous* state. __Stars are made up of matter in the plasma state.__

4. An object's density is equal to its mass divided by its *length*. __An object's density is equal to its mass divided by its volume.__

5. Matter with atoms in a fixed position in relation to one another is in the *liquid* state. __Matter with atoms in a fixed position in relation to one another is in the solid state.__

6. Density and state of matter are *chemical* properties. __Density and state of matter are physical properties.__

7. *Hydrogen* is the only substance that occurs naturally on Earth as a gas, a liquid, and a solid. __Water is the only substance that occurs naturally on Earth as a gas, a liquid, and a solid.__

8. The *physical* properties of a liquid do not change when it becomes a gas. __The chemical properties of a liquid do not change when it becomes a gas.__

9. *Liquids* fill their entire container regardless of the container's size or shape. __Gases fill their entire container regardless of the container's size or shape.__

10. On Earth the *solid* state of matter is least common. __On Earth the plasma state of matter is least common.__

Chapter 2

STUDY GUIDE ● **Energy from Atoms**

Match each description in Column I with the correct term in Column II. Write the letter of the correct term in the blank at the left.

Column I

Column II
a. fission
b. Rocky Mountains
c. neutrons
d. fuel rods
e. uranium-235 isotope
f. Yucca Mountain
g. nuclear waste
h. sandstone
i. nuclear energy
j. fossil fuels

b 1. Location of ore deposits used to make fuel for nuclear reactors

d 2. Long metal pipes that sit in water in a nuclear reactor

a 3. The splitting of the nuclei of heavy elements

f 4. Site of a proposed nuclear waste storage facility

____ 5. Source of most of the electricity generated by power plants in the United States

h 6. Source of rock used to make fuel for nuclear power plants

e 7. Most commonly used fuel in fission power plants

g 8. Highly radioactive material produced by nuclear power plants

c 9. Particles that begin a heat-releasing chain reaction when fired into fuel rods in a nuclear reactor

____ 10. Energy source produced from nuclear reactions

Answer the following questions on the lines provided.

11. What are three major hazards for possible nuclear waste storage sites? __Three hazards for possible nuclear waste storage sites are volcanoes, earthquakes, and groundwater seepage.__

12. How is heat released during an atomic reaction used to produce electricity in a nuclear reactor? __The heat is used to boil water. The resulting steam drives a turbine, which turns a generator, producing electricity.__

13. Why do some people oppose plans by the U.S. Department of Energy to construct a nuclear waste storage facility in Nevada? __Critics are concerned that water could reach the deeply buried storage site, possibly as a result of an earthquake along one of the faults that run through the area. Water could corrode the containers in which the waste is stored and release toxic waste.__

Chapter 3

STUDY GUIDE

• Minerals

Find the error in each statement. Rewrite the statement correctly on the line provided.

1. A mineral is a solid that comes from organic matter. **A mineral is a solid that comes from inorganic matter.**

2. Salt, diamonds, graphite, and coal are minerals. **Salt, diamonds, and graphite are minerals.**

3. The compounds in a mineral are arranged in a repeating pattern to form crystals. **The atoms in a mineral are arranged in a repeating pattern to form crystals.**

4. Some minerals form from magma, which is hot, liquid rock material on Earth's surface. **Some minerals form from magma, which is hot, liquid rock material beneath Earth's surface.**

5. Halite crystals are formed when fresh lake water evaporates. **Halite crystals are formed when salt water evaporates.**

6. The smallest group of rock-forming minerals consists of silicates. **The largest group of rock-forming minerals consists of silicates.**

In the blank at the left, write the term in the box that correctly completes each statement.

crystal	halide	silicates	4000	8
carbonates	elements	oxides	98 percent	6

_____4000_____   7. Scientists know of more than _____ minerals.

_____8_____   8. Most of these are composed of only _____ elements.

_____98 percent_____   9. These few elements make up _____ of Earth's crust.

_____silicates_____   10. Minerals that combine to form the most common rock-forming group are _____.

_____halide_____   11. A group that includes rock salt is the _____ group.

_____crystal_____   12. Each mineral has a different _____ formation.

_____6_____   13. Scientists have identified _____ major formation systems.

_____carbonates; oxides_____   14. Two other major groups of minerals are _____ and _____.

Chapter 3

STUDY GUIDE

• Mineral Identification

Match the terms in Column I with the phrases in Column II. Write the letter of the correct phrase in the blank on the left.

Column I

g   1. cleavage

d   2. diamond

i   3. fracture

a   4. hardness

h   5. mica

e   6. luster

b   7. Mohs

j   8. quartz

f   9. streak

c   10. talc

Column II

a. The measure of how easily a mineral can be scratched

b. Name given to the scale of hardness

c. One of the softest known minerals

d. The hardest known mineral

e. Reflection of light from a mineral's surface

f. Color left by powdered mineral on unglazed porcelain

g. Tendency to break along smooth, flat surfaces

h. A common mineral that breaks along smooth, flat surfaces

i. Tendency to break with rough or jagged edges

j. A common mineral that breaks with rough or jagged edges

Answer the following question on the lines provided.

11. What three tests would you perform to help you identify an unknown mineral?

1. Use the Mohs scale to measure hardness. Experiment to see which minerals the sample will scratch and which will scratch the sample.

2. Examine the mineral's streak on unglazed porcelain.

3. Identify the luster of the unknown mineral as metallic or nonmetallic and describe it. Other correct answers include: Examine its color. See if the sample shows cleavage or fracture.

In the blanks at the left, write the terms that correctly complete each statement.

pyrite; gold   12. The mineral _____ is sometimes confused with gold because both minerals are the color of _____.

graphite; pencils   13. The mineral _____ is soft enough to leave a streak on paper and is commonly used in _____.

Chapter 3

STUDY GUIDE

Text Pages 74–77

● Uses of Minerals

Use the words in the box to fill in the blanks. Some words may be used more than once.

aluminum	amethyst	crystal
expense	gems	ores
profit	rare	supply
traces	useful	value

Stones called **gems** _____ are highly prized minerals because they are beautiful and often **rare** _____. Many gemstones have a **crystal** _____ structure that allows them to be cut and **polished** _____ to the high quality needed for jewelry. The difference between a gemstone and the common form of the same mineral is sometimes slight. The purple stone **amethyst** _____, for example, is quartz with just **traces** _____ of iron in its structure.

Some minerals contain a **useful** _____ substance that can be mined at a **profit** _____. Such minerals are called **ores** _____. Bauxite is this kind of mineral because **aluminum** _____ can be taken from it and made into **useful** _____ products. In most cases, waste rock or material must be removed before a mineral can be used. If the **expense** _____ of mining gets higher than the **value** _____ of the material, the mineral is no longer considered to be an ore. The value of the material can also change if the **supply** _____ or the demand increases or decreases.

Use words in the box at the top of the page that fit to complete the puzzle.

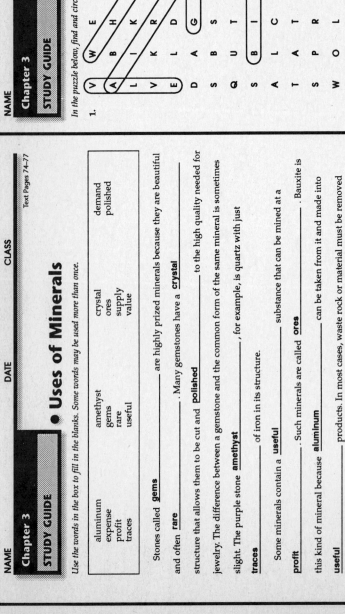

```
      P   R   O   F   I   T   S
  A   L   U   M   I   N   U   M
          A   M   E   T   H   Y   S   T
              O   R   E   S
          T   R   A   C   E   S
  C   R   Y   S   T   A   L
```

Chapter 3

STUDY GUIDE

Text Pages 78–84

● Uses of Titanium

In the puzzle below, find and circle eight examples of things that can be made of titanium.

1.

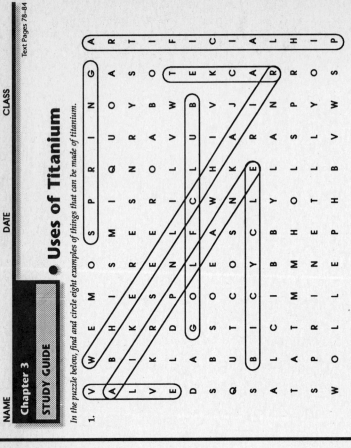

```
V   W   E   M   O   S   P   R   I   N   G   A
A   B   H   I   S   M   I   Q   U   O   A   R
L   I   K   E   R   E   S   N   R   Y   S   T
V   K   R   S   E   E   R   O   A   B   O   I
E   L   D   P   N   L   I   L   V   W   T   F
D   A   G   O   L   F   C   L   U   B   E   I
S   B   S   O   E   A   W   H   I   V   K   C
Q   U   T   C   O   S   N   K   A   J   C   I
S   B   I   C   Y   C   L   E   R   I   A   A
A   L   C   I   B   B   Y   L   A   N   R   L
T   A   T   M   H   O   L   S   P   R   H
S   P   R   I   N   E   T   L   Y   O
W   O   L   L   E   P   H   B   V   W   S   P
```

Answer the following questions on the lines provided.

2. Why are many artificial body parts made of titanium? **Titanium is useful in biomedicine because** _____ **it is durable, lightweight, and nontoxic.** _____

3. Why are manufacturers more likely to obtain titanium from rutile than from ilmenite? **The process used for obtaining titanium from ilmenite produces a substance that is harmful to** _____ **the environment, whereas the process for obtaining titanium from rutile does not.** _____

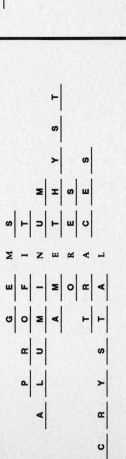

Chapter 4
STUDY GUIDE

● The Rock Cycle

Match the items in Column I with the terms in Column II. Write the letter of the correct term in the blank at the left.

Column I

Column II

__b__ 1. A naturally occurring, nonliving solid with a definite structure and composition

__a__ 2. A mixture of minerals, mineraloids, glass, or organic matter

__e__ 3. Processes by which rocks form and change

__c__ 4. A hard silicate mineral

__d__ 5. An igneous rock made up of mica, feldspar, quartz, and hornblende

a. rock
b. mineral
c. quartz
d. granite
e. rock cycle

In the blank, write the term that correctly completes each sentence. Use the information in the textbook.

6. If the minerals in a sedimentary rock melt and then cool, they can form a(n) __igneous__ rock.

7. Quartz is a common __mineral__ found in rocks.

8. Sedimentary and igneous rocks can be changed into metamorphic rocks by __heat__ and __pressure__.

9. If an igneous rock weathers and erodes into fragments, the fragments can form a(n) __sedimentary__ rock.

10. Weathering and erosion are two of the __processes__ that change rocks.

Write each word in the box under the correct heading.

weathering	melting	cooling
erosion	compaction	cementation
deposition	metamorphic	

Processes in the rock cycle

weathering __heating__

deposition __compaction__

melting __cooling__

erosion __cementation__

Kinds of rocks

sedimentary

__igneous__

__metamorphic__

Chapter 4
STUDY GUIDE

● Igneous Rocks

Use the words in the box to fill in the blanks

200	iron	lava
fine	1400	dense
magma	large	abundant
formation	surface	granitic
basaltic	radioactive	pressure
intrusive	extrusive	magnification

Most __magma__ originates 60 to __200 km__ below Earth's surface. Temperatures reach about __1400__ °C at these depths.

In certain locations, __pressure__ and heat caused by overlying rocks and __radioactive__ elements produce magma. Rocks formed from molten Earth materials are __igneous__ rocks. When magma cools below Earth's surface, it forms __large__ grained, __intrusive__ igneous rocks. The __crystals__ of these common rocks grow large because of the __slow__ rate of cooling. When magma moves to Earth's __surface__, it is called __lava__. When lava cools on Earth's surface, it forms __fine__ grained, __extrusive__ igneous rocks. Minerals of extrusive rocks are so small that __magnification__ is needed for identification. Igneous rocks can be classified by their __formation__. They can also be classified by the types of __minerals__ in them.

__Basaltic__ igneous rocks are dark-colored, heavy, and __dense__. They contain __iron__ and magnesium. __Granitic__ igneous rocks are __lighter__ colored and less dense. They contain a lot of oxygen and __silicon__. Igneous rocks are the most __abundant__ on Earth.

Sedimentary Rocks

Chapter 4

STUDY GUIDE

Text Pages 101–107

Answer the following questions on the lines provided.

1. What are sediments? **Sediments are loose materials such as rock fragments, mineral grains, and bits of plant and animal remains that have been transported by erosion processes.**

2. What are sedimentary rocks? **They are rocks that form when sediments are pressed or cemented together or fall out of solution.**

3. What is compaction? **Compaction is the process by which small sediments are pressed together to form solid rock.**

4. What is cementation? **Cementation is the process by which large sediments are glued together to form solid rock.**

5. What are detrital sedimentary rocks? **They are rocks made of broken fragments of plants, animals, and other rocks.**

6. What is conglomerate? **Conglomerate is a detrital rock formed from large, well-rounded sediments.**

7. What is breccia? **Breccia is a detrital rock formed from large sediments with sharp angles.**

8. What are chemical sedimentary rocks? **They are rocks formed from minerals dissolved in solution.**

9. What are organic sedimentary rocks? **They are rocks formed from the remains of once-living things.**

10. What is coquina? **Coquina is limestone formed from large shell fragments.**

11. What is chalk? **Chalk is limestone formed from tiny shells.**

20

Metamorphic Rocks

Chapter 4

STUDY GUIDE

Text Pages 97–100

Determine whether each of the following statements is true or false. Write the word "true" or "false" in the blank. If the sentence is false, rewrite it so that it is true.

true   1. Metamorphic rocks are rocks that have been changed by temperature and pressure.

false   2. Nonfoliated rock will separate easily into layers. **Foliated rock will separate easily into layers.**

false   3. Pressure does not play a role in the formation of metamorphic rocks. **Pressure does play a role in forming metamorphic rocks.**

true   4. A metamorphic rock with a foliated texture has bands of minerals.

true   5. Metamorphic rocks can be formed from changes in igneous, sedimentary, or other metamorphic rocks.

false   6. Sandstone is a metamorphic rock. **Sandstone is a sedimentary rock.**

true   7. A metamorphic rock with no banding is nonfoliated.

true   8. The mineral grains in metamorphic rocks may be flattened.

Complete the chart using information in your textbook.

Type of rock	Can change into	Metamorphic rock
Sedimentary		
Shale	→	schist
Sandstone	→	quartzite
Igneous		
Basalt	→	schist
Granite	→	gneiss
Metamorphic		
Slate	→	schist

19

Chapter 4

STUDY GUIDE

● Burning Waste Coal

Answer the following questions on the lines provided.

1. How does the process of cogeneration differ from other processes for generating power? __In the process of cogeneration, both the electrical energy and the thermal energy generated__ __are used.__

2. What problems are caused by the piles of waste coal found near abandoned coal mines? __Piles of waste coal are unsightly and can generate acid runoff.__

Put an X by each statement that does not agree with your textbook.

_____ 3. Coal is an organic sedimentary rock.

__X__ 4. Coal no longer provides fuel for electricity in the United States.

__X__ 5. Waste coal is the result of new mining techniques.

_____ 6. Acid runoff results when rain flows through piles of waste coal.

_____ 7. Mixing waste coal with limestone before burning removes more than 90 percent of harmful sulfur dioxide emissions.

_____ 8. The ash that results from burning waste coal changes to a low-grade cement when it mixes with water.

__X__ 9. Some companies use waste coal to generate electrical energy, but the thermal energy that is generated cannot be used.

__X__ 10. Waste coal is what remains after coal is burned.

Chapter 5

STUDY GUIDE

● Landforms

Answer the following questions on the lines provided.

1. What are the three basic types of landforms? __plains, plateaus, and mountains__

2. What are the four types of mountains? __folded, upwarped, fault-block, and volcanic__

Match each description in Column I with the correct term in Column II. Write the letter of the correct term in the blank at the left.

Column I

__b__ 3. Large, relatively flat areas of land

__f__ 4. Large areas of horizontal rocks that have been uplifted and that rise steeply above the land around the rocks

__e__ 5. Distance above or below sea level

__c__ 6. Grassy wetlands usually flooded with water

__i__ 7. Broad, flat lowlands along coastlines

__h__ 8. Land features that rise high above the surrounding land

__a__ 9. Type of mountains formed when rock layers are squeezed from opposite sides

__j__ 10. Type of mountains formed when crust was pushed up by forces inside Earth

__d__ 11. Type of mountains formed when huge tilted blocks of rocks are separated from surrounding rock by faults

__g__ 12. Type of mountains formed when molten material reaches Earth's surface through a weak area in the crust

Column II

a. folded mountains

b. plains

c. marshes

d. fault-block mountains

e. elevation

f. plateaus

g. volcanic mountains

h. mountains

i. coastal plains

j. upwarped mountains

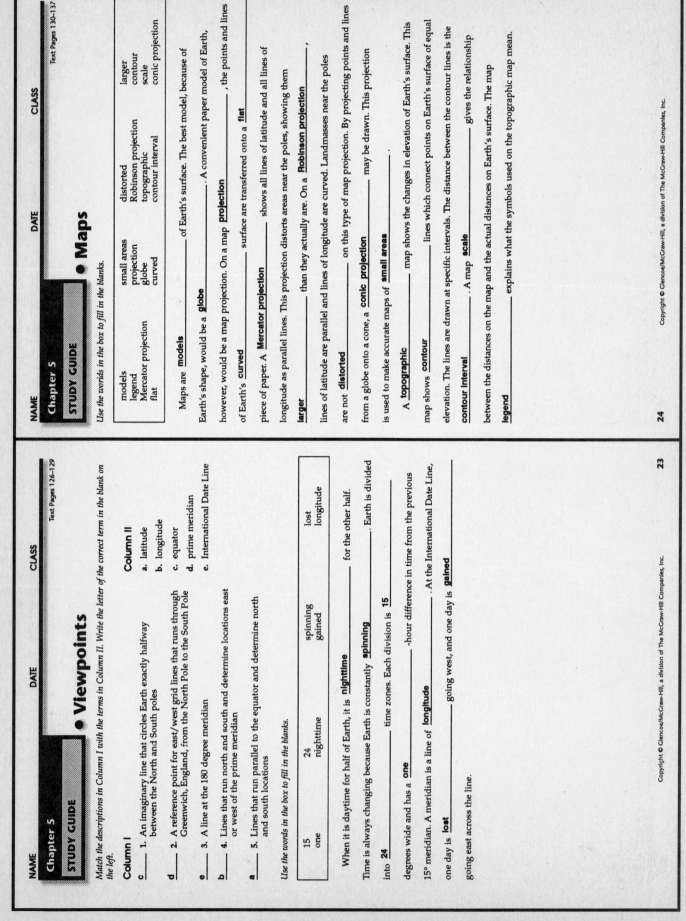

NAME _____ **DATE** _____ **CLASS** _____

Chapter 5

STUDY GUIDE

● Viewpoints

Match the descriptions in Column I with the terms in Column II. Write the letter of the correct term in the blank on the left.

Column I

c ___ 1. An imaginary line that circles Earth exactly halfway between the North and South poles

d ___ 2. A reference point for east/west grid lines that runs through Greenwich, England, from the North Pole to the South Pole

e ___ 3. A line at the 180 degree meridian

b ___ 4. Lines that run north and south and determine locations east or west of the prime meridian

a ___ 5. Lines that run parallel to the equator and determine north and south locations

Column II

a. latitude

b. longitude

c. equator

d. prime meridian

e. International Date Line

Use the words in the box to fill in the blanks.

15	spinning	lost
one	gained	longitude
24	nighttime	

When it is daytime for half of Earth, it is **nighttime** _____ for the other half.

Time is always changing because Earth is constantly **spinning** _____. Earth is divided

into **24** _____ time zones. Each division is **15** _____

degrees wide and has a **one** _____ -hour difference in time from the previous

15° meridian. A meridian is a line of **longitude** _____. At the International Date Line,

one day is **lost** _____ going west, and one day is **gained** _____

going east across the line.

NAME _____ **DATE** _____ **CLASS** _____

Chapter 5

STUDY GUIDE

● Maps

Use the words in the box to fill in the blanks.

models	small areas	distorted	larger
legend	projection	Robinson projection	contour
Mercator projection	globe	topographic	scale
flat	curved	contour interval	conic projection

Maps are **models** _____ of Earth's surface. The best model, because of

Earth's shape, would be a **globe** _____. A convenient paper model of Earth,

however, would be a map projection. On a map **projection** _____, the points and lines

of Earth's **curved** _____ surface are transferred onto a **flat** _____

piece of paper. A **Mercator projection** _____ shows all lines of latitude and all lines of

longitude as parallel lines. This projection distorts areas near the poles, showing them

larger _____ than they actually are. On a **Robinson projection** _____,

lines of latitude are parallel and lines of longitude are curved. Landmasses near the poles

are not **distorted** _____ on this type of map projection. By projecting points and lines

from a globe onto a cone, a **conic projection** _____ may be drawn. This projection

is used to make accurate maps of **small areas** _____.

A **topographic** _____ map shows the changes in elevation of Earth's surface. This

map shows **contour** _____ lines which connect points on Earth's surface of equal

elevation. The lines are drawn at specific intervals. The distance between the contour lines is the

contour interval _____. A map **scale** _____ gives the relationship

between the distances on the map and the actual distances on Earth's surface. The map

legend _____ explains what the symbols used on the topographic map mean.

Chapter 6

STUDY GUIDE

● Weathering

Use the words to fill in the blanks of the paragraphs.

plants	pieces	moisture	ice wedging	acids	carbonic acid
freezing	chemical	oxidation	temperatures	minerals	
climate	desert	mechanical	cracks	reacting	

Weathering is the breaking of rocks into **pieces** _____. There are two main types of weathering. **Mechanical** _____ weathering involves breaking rocks without changing their chemical composition. In **ice wedging** _____, water trapped in rocks freezes and expands, forcing the rocks apart. **Plants** _____ can also cause mechanical weathering. As their roots grow and put pressure on rocks, **cracks** _____ widen and rock fragments may fall off. **Chemical** _____ weathering involves water, air, and other substances' **reacting** _____ with the minerals in the rocks. When metal is exposed to water and oxygen, **oxidation** _____ occurs and rust forms. **Acids** _____ in plant roots and mosses can also react with the **minerals** _____ in rocks. Water and carbon dioxide combine to form **carbonic acid** _____, which reacts with minerals such as calcite in limestone. How rapidly weathering occurs in an area depends on the **climate** _____. Chemical weathering happens more slowly in **desert** _____ areas due to a lack of **moisture** _____. Low **temperatures** _____ in polar regions keep chemical weathering to a minimum there. Whenever **freezing** _____ and thawing alternate, mechanical weathering becomes an important form of weathering.

26

Chapter 5

STUDY GUIDE

● Mapping Our Planet

Use the words in the box to complete the statements.

radar	Sea Beam	distance
ocean	calculated	dozen
sound	speed	gravitational force
receiving	Landsat	colors
Topex-Poseidon	echo	time

1. A **Landsat** _____ Satellite uses a mirror to detect wavelengths of energy reflected from Earth's surface.

2. The **Topex-Poseidon** _____ Satellite computes the distance between the satellite and the ocean's surface.

3. The high-frequency radio waves that are transmitted by the Topex-Poseidon Satellite are also known as **radar** _____ waves.

4. Information gathered from Landsat satellites is used to show different wavelengths of energy as **colors** _____.

5. Ocean water forms bulges over mountains and depressions over valleys because there is more **gravitational force** _____ between ocean water and large structures on the ocean floor.

6. **Sea Beam** _____ is a new sonar technology.

7. Sonar refers to the use of **sound** _____ waves to detect structures on the **ocean** _____ bottom.

8. Sea Beam sends a **sound** _____ wave from the bottom of the ship toward the **ocean** _____ floor.

9. The sound wave bounces off the ocean floor and an **echo** _____ device.
wave is picked up by a **receiving** _____ device.

10. The **distance** _____ the sound wave traveled is **calculated** _____ by a computer.

11. The computer uses the **speed** _____ of the sound in the water and the **time** _____ it takes for the sound to be reflected to make the calculations.

12. An equipped Sea Beam has more than a **dozen** _____ sonar devices.

25

Chapter 6

STUDY GUIDE

• Soil

Use the terms in the box to complete the sentences. Use the information in your textbook.

soil	humus	A horizon
horizons	composition	below
topsoil	parent	top
evolve	bottom	leaching
soil profile	water	

1. **Soil** _____ is a mixture of sediments of weathered rock and organic matter.

2. Decaying plant and animal matter is called **humus** _____.

3. Due to weathering, different layers, or **horizons** _____, of soil form.

4. Soil generally has three layers, and these make up a **soil profile** _____.

5. The A horizon is the **top** _____ layer and is also known as **topsoil** _____.

6. The B horizon is the layer **below** _____ the A horizon.

7. The C horizon is the **bottom** _____ weathered rock but no humus.

8. Below the bottom horizon is **parent** _____ rock.

9. You can tell that the **A Horizon** _____ is the most fully evolved soil layer because it has more humus and smaller rock fragments than the other layers.

10. **Water** _____ moving downward through the horizons dissolves and carries minerals into lower horizons by the process of **leaching** _____.

11. The thickness of the soil layers and their **composition** _____ depend on the climate, slope of the land, and the type of rock in an area and how long the soil has been evolving.

12. Soil horizons **evolve** _____ more slowly in an area that has little rainfall because chemical weathering occurs slowly in a dry climate.

Chapter 6

STUDY GUIDE

• Land Use and Soil Loss

Match the items in Column I with the terms in Column II. Write the letter of the correct term in the blank at the left.

Column I

___e___ 1. Practice of leaving plant stalks in the field

___a___ 2. Mechanical turning and loosening of the soil

___b___ 3. Trees and plants in tropical regions

___d___ 4. Desert formation

___c___ 5. Practice of alternating crops that cover the ground with crops that leave the land exposed

Column II

a. plowing

b. rain forest

c. strip cropping

d. desertification

e. no-till farming

Decide whether each of the following statements is true or false. Write the word "true" or "false" in the blank. If the statement is false, rewrite it so that it is true.

___true___ 6. Soil loss is particularly severe in the tropics.

_____

___true___ 7. Plants are important to soil, because without them, soil evolution stops and no new soil develops.

_____

_____

___false___ 8. Desertification is a slow process that affects very little land each year.
Desertification is a rapid process that affects a lot of land each year.

_____

___false___ 9. In dry areas, farmers minimize soil erosion by plowing under the natural vegetation. **In dry areas, farmers minimize soil erosion by grazing the land instead of plowing under the natural vegetation to plant crops.**

_____

___false___ 10. Soil can easily recover the nutrients that crops use up.
Soil takes years to recover the nutrients that crops use up.

_____

_____

110

Text Pages 172-179

● Gravity

Solve the following crossword puzzle by using the clues provided.

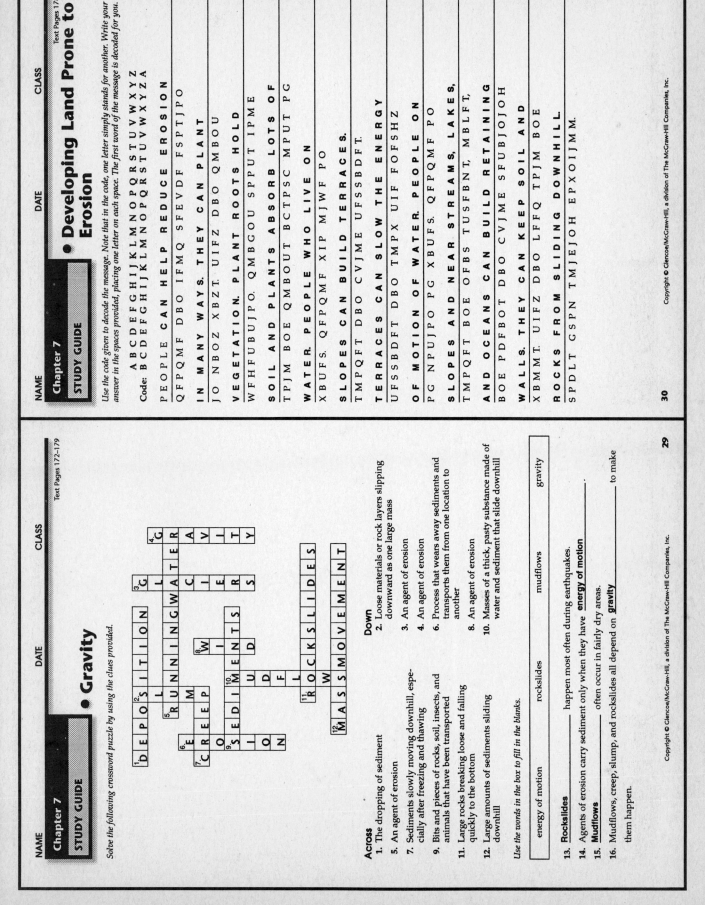

Across

1. The dropping of sediment
5. An agent of erosion
7. Sediments slowly moving downhill, especially after freezing and thawing
9. Bits and pieces of rocks, soil, insects, and animals that have been transported
11. Large rocks breaking loose and falling quickly to the bottom
12. Large amounts of sediments sliding downhill

Down

2. Loose materials or rock layers slipping downward as one large mass
3. An agent of erosion
4. An agent of erosion
6. Process that wears away sediments and transports them from one location to another
8. An agent of erosion
10. Masses of a thick, pasty substance made of water and sediment that slide downhill

Use the words in the box to fill in the blanks.

| energy of motion | rockslides | mudflows | gravity |

13. **Rockslides** ___ happen most often during earthquakes.
14. Agents of erosion carry sediment only when they have **energy of motion** .
15. **Mudflows** ___ often occur in fairly dry areas.
16. Mudflows, creep, slump, and rockslides all depend on **gravity** ___ to make them happen.

Text Pages 178-179

● Developing Land Prone to Erosion

Use the code given to decode the message. Note that in the code, one letter simply stands for another. Write your answer in the spaces provided, placing one letter on each space. The first word of the message is decoded for you.

```
     A B C D E F G H I J K L M N O P Q R S T U V W X Y Z
Code: B C D E F G H I J K L M N O P Q R S T U V W X Y Z A
```

PEOPLE CAN HELP REDUCE EROSION
QFPQMF DBO IFMQ SFEVDF FSPTJPO

IN MANY WAYS. THEY CAN PLANT
JO NBOZ XBZT. UIFZ DBO QMBOU

VEGETATION. PLANT ROOTS HOLD
WFHFUBUJPO. QMBOU SPPUT IPME

SOIL AND PLANTS ABSORB LOTS OF
TPJM BOE QMBOUT BCTPSC MPUT PG

WATER. PEOPLE WHO LIVE ON
XBUFS. QFPQMF XIP MJWF PO

SLOPES CAN BUILD TERRACES.
TMPQFT DBO CVJME UFSSBDFT.

TERRACES CAN SLOW THE ENERGY
UFSSBDFT DBO TMPX UIF FOFSHZ

OF MOTION OF WATER. PEOPLE ON
PG NPUJPO PG XBUFS. QFPQMF PO

SLOPES AND NEAR STREAMS, LAKES,
TMPQFT BOE OFBS TUSFBNT, MBLFT,

AND OCEANS CAN BUILD RETAINING
BOE PDFBOT DBO CVJME SFUBJOJOH

WALLS. THEY CAN KEEP SOIL AND
XBMMT. UIFZ DBO LFFQ TPJM BOE

ROCKS FROM SLIDING DOWNHILL
SPDLT GSPN TMJEJOH EPXOIJMM.

111

Chapter 7
STUDY GUIDE

● Glaciers

Determine whether each of the following statements is true or false. Write the word "true" or "false" in the blank. If the statement is false, change the italicized term to make the statement true.

true 1. The glaciers in Greenland and Antarctica are *continental glaciers.*

false 2. The usually long, parallel scars gouged into bedrock by glaciers are known as *cirques.* **grooves or striations**

false 3. Valleys eroded by glaciers are usually *V-shaped.* **U-shaped**

true 4. *Till* is the sediments that drop from the base of a glacier as it stops moving.

false 5. Moraines are mounds of material formed by deposits of glacial *outwash.* **till**

true 6. Meltwater forms a winding ridge of sand and gravel known as an *esker.*

true 7. Glacial *plucking* can create a cirque, or bowl-shaped basin, on a mountainside.

false 8. One type of *till* deposits is an alluvial fan of glacially eroded sediments. **outwash**

true 9. *Icebergs* are sources of fresh water.

true 10. *Plucking* is the process by which rocks and soil are added to the sides and bottom of a glacier when water freezes and melts.

false 11. Very large striations are called glacial *cracks.* **grooves**

true 12. The two types of glacial *deposits* are till and outwash.

false 13. Scientists have been studying ways to tow *valley glaciers.* **icebergs**

true 14. The Great Lakes were gouged out by *glacial ice.*

Chapter 7
STUDY GUIDE

● Wind

The important ideas in a textbook chapter often are easier to understand if you organize them into a chart. The chart can also help you better remember the information. The chart that follows is on erosion and deposition by the wind. It is only partially filled in. Use the headings and the information provided in Chapter 7 to complete the chart.

Wind erosion

Type: deflation
Description: **The pickup and movement of small sediments like clay, silt, and sand by the wind**
Type: abrasion
Description: **The mechanical weathering of rock by windblown sand and other rock particles**

Deposition by the wind

Type: loess
Description: **Deposits of fine-grained particles that are tightly packed**
Type: dunes
Description: **Windblown sand that piles up behind an obstacle**

Use the types of wind erosion and deposition to complete these statements.

1. Wind erosion similar to sandblasting is **abrasion** .

2. Some midwestern farmland in the United States is covered by **loess** .

3. The most common wind deposits are **dunes** .

4. In **deflation** , wind picks up and moves small sediments but leaves heavier pebbles and rocks behind.

5. Tightly packed wind deposits of fine particles are called **loess** .

6. Sand **dunes** are constantly changing and moving as the wind erodes them.

7. **Abrasion** causes the pitting and polishing of rocks and sediments.

8. Both abrasion and **deflation** are common in areas where there are few plants to protect sediments.

Chapter 8

STUDY GUIDE

Text Pages 206–209

● Surface Water

In the blank at the left, write the letter of the term or phrase that correctly completes each statement.

c 1. Water runoff forms small _____.
   a. water cycles b. drainage c. streams d. overflows

b 2. The land area from which a stream gets its water is its _____.
   a. overflow b. drainage basin c. runoff d. river system

d 3. The largest drainage basin in the United States is that of the _____.
   a. Missouri River c. Appalachian Mountains
   b. Rocky Mountains d. Mississippi River

a 4. Most of the rain that falls between the Rocky Mountains and the Appalachian Mountains flows into the _____.
   a. Missouri and Ohio rivers c. Rocky Mountains
   b. Appalachian Mountains d. Pacific Ocean

d 5. A stream that flows swiftly through a steep valley is a _____ stream.
   a. mature b. shallow c. old d. young

a 6. The broad, flat valley floor cut by a stream is a _____.
   a. floodplain b. meander c. drainage system d. mature river

b 7. A curve in the river formed by erosion is called a _____.
   a. floodplain b. meander c. drainage system d. mature river

The diagrams show young, mature, or old rivers. Label each diagram correctly.

8. **old**   9. **young**   10. **mature**

Chapter 8

STUDY GUIDE

Text Pages 214–218

● Groundwater

In the blank at the left, write a term from the list to match each definition.

aquifer	geyser	impermeable	artesian
groundwater	permeable	water table	cave
hot spring	carbonic acid	zone of saturation	spring

groundwater 1. Water that collects underground

permeable 2. Word describing soil or rock through which water can pass

impermeable 3. Word describing soil or rock through which water cannot pass

aquifer 4. Layer of rock that transmits water freely

zone of saturation 5. Area where all pores in the rock are filled with water

water table 6. Upper surface of the area where all the pores in the rock are filled with water

artesian 7. Type of well in which water under pressure rises to the surface

spring 8. Area where the water table meets Earth's surface and flows out

hot spring 9. Area where heated groundwater comes to the surface

geyser 10. Hot spring that erupts periodically

carbonic acid 11. Weak acid that forms when water mixes with carbon dioxide

cave 12. Underground opening formed when acid groundwater dissolves limestone

Use the words in the box to fill in the blanks.

calcite	stalactites	evaporates
stalagmites	limestone	

Groundwater continues to affect the **limestone** _____ rock that forms a cave. It drips slowly from cracks in the cave walls and ceilings. Sometimes this water **evaporates** _____ while dripping from the roof of a cave. It leaves deposits of **calcite** _____. These deposits grow down from the cave's ceiling and form **stalactites** _____. If the water drips to the cave floor and then evaporates, it leaves deposits that grow up from the floor. These are called **stalagmites** _____.

Chapter 8

STUDY GUIDE ● Water Wars

Match the definitions in Column I with the terms in Column II. Write the letter of the correct term in the blank on the left.

Column I

Column II

e __ 1. Use of water for fishing or boating

a. agricultural use

c __ 2. Use of water for manufacturing

b. freshwater

d __ 3. Change of the natural flow of water

c. industrial use

b __ 4. Water that is not salt water

d. water diversion

a __ 5. Use of water to grow crops

e. recreational use

Read the sentences that follow and unscramble the terms.

1. When the natural flow of water is changed by people, it is called trewa verdision. __water diversion__

2. As the population grows, greater demand is put on Earth's rewfserath supply. __freshwater__

3. One reason people divert water is because they have a water gheators. __shortage__

Answer the following questions on the lines provided.

1. What change in population has made some people think about diverting water from the Great Lakes? __The centers of the greatest population growth are in the South.__

2. How would that water diversion affect the states on the Great Lakes? __There would be less water available for industry, agriculture, recreation, and home use.__

Chapter 8

STUDY GUIDE ● Ocean Shoreline

Each numbered list below gives some characteristics of one of the shoreline features in the box. Write the name of each shoreline feature above the correct list.

> shoreline   beach   longshore current
> rocky shoreline   barrier islands

1. __rocky shoreline__
   - rocks
   - cliffs
   - caves

2. __longshore current__
   - colliding waves
   - running water
   - parallel to shore

3. __shoreline__
   - high tide
   - low tide
   - water's edge

4. __barrier islands__
   - sand deposits
   - separated from mainland
   - dunes

5. __beach__
   - smooth, gently sloping
   - sediment deposits
   - sands

A cause is something that makes something happen. An effect is what happens. Write the part of the statement that is the cause and the part that is the effect on the lines provided.

1. Shorelines change constantly because they experience the forces of tides, waves, and currents.

   cause: __Tides, waves, and currents are forces on shorelines.__

   effect: __Shorelines change constantly.__

2. When constant wave motion bumps sand grains together, the corners of the sand become rounded.

   cause: __Constant wave motion bumps sand grains together.__

   effect: __The corners of the sand become rounded.__

3. The more energy a longshore current has, the more it will erode shoreline sediments.

   cause: __A longshore current has extra energy.__

   effect: __More shoreline sediments will be eroded.__

4. Beaches have sand-sized particles because waves break rocks and seashells down.

   cause: __Waves break rocks and seashells down.__

   effect: __Beaches have sand-sized particles.__

Chapter 9

STUDY GUIDE

Forces Inside Earth

On the line above each illustration, label the type of fault shown—normal fault, reverse fault, and strike-slip fault. Then below each illustration put the numbers of the fault's characteristics from the list.

1. Tension pulls rocks apart.
2. Compression pushes rocks in.
3. Shearing forces push rocks from different, but not opposite, directions.
4. This kind of fault occurs at transform fault boundaries.
5. This kind of fault occurs at divergent plate boundaries.
6. This kind of fault occurs at convergent plate boundaries.
7. Rocks above the fault surface are forced up and over the rocks below the fault surface.
8. Rocks above the fault surface move downward in relation to rocks below the fault surface.
9. Rocks on either side of the fault boundary move past each other without much upward or downward movement.
10. Many of these faults occurred when the Sierra Nevadas were formed.
11. The Himalaya Mountains contain many of these faults.
12. The San Andreas Fault is an example of this kind of fault.
13. Rocks become twisted and strained when they snag each other.

normal fault

reverse fault

strike-slip fault

1 _____   2 _____   3 _____
5 _____   6 _____   4 _____
8 _____   7 _____   9 _____
10 _____ 11 _____ 12 _____
          13 _____

Chapter 9

STUDY GUIDE

Earthquake Information

Solve the crossword puzzle by using the clues provided.

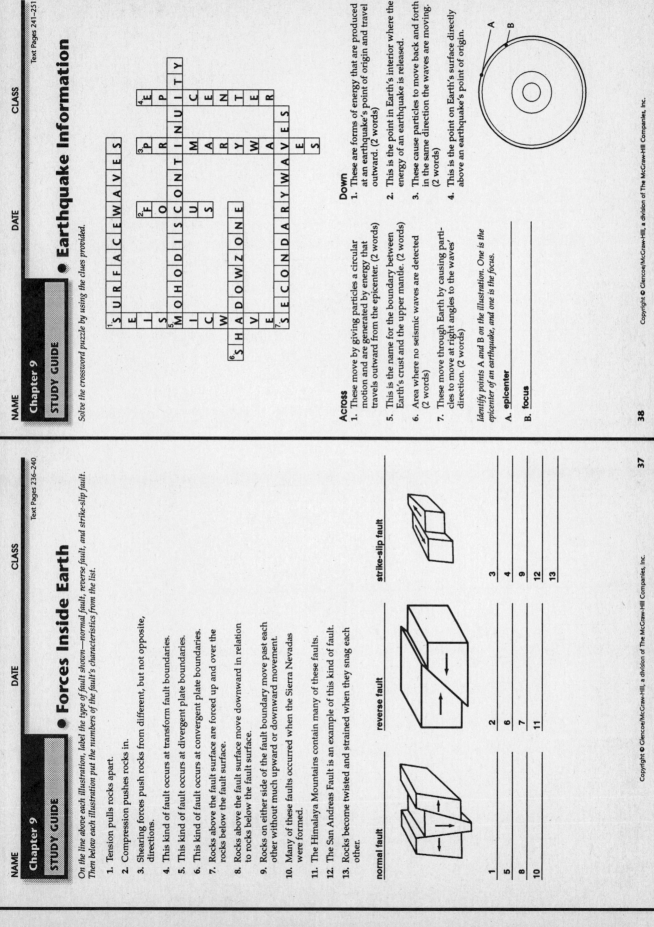

Across

1. These move by giving particles a circular motion and are generated by energy that travels outward from the epicenter. (2 words)
5. This is the name for the boundary between Earth's crust and the upper mantle. (2 words)
6. Area where no seismic waves are detected (2 words)
7. These move through Earth by causing particles to move at right angles to the waves' direction. (2 words)

Down

1. These are forms of energy that are produced at an earthquake's point of origin and travel outward. (2 words)
2. This is the point in Earth's interior where the energy of an earthquake is released.
3. These cause particles to move back and forth in the same direction the waves are moving. (2 words)
4. This is the point on Earth's surface directly above an earthquake's point of origin.

Identify points A and B on the illustration. One is the epicenter of an earthquake, and one is the focus.

A. **epicenter**

B. **focus**

115

Chapter 9

STUDY GUIDE

• Destruction by Earthquakes

Rewrite each sentence by changing the italicized word or words to make the sentence correct.

1. A *Richter Scale* is an instrument that is used to record primary, secondary, and surface waves of an earthquake. **A seismograph is an instrument that is used to record primary, secondary, and surface waves of an earthquake.**

2. An earthquake's *severity* is the measure of the energy released by the earthquake. **An earthquake's magnitude is the measure of the energy released by the earthquake.**

3. Seismic sea waves are also called *secondary waves*. **Seismic sea waves are also called tsunamis.**

4. A scientist who studies earthquakes is a *seismograph*. **A scientist who studies earthquakes is a seismologist.**

5. Scientists use the *Moho Scale* to measure the magnitude of earthquakes. **Scientists use the Richter Scale to measure the magnitude of earthquakes.**

6. The earthquake in Kansu, China, registered 8.5 on the Richter Scale and released *ten* times more energy that the one in Messina, Italy, that registered 7.5. **The earthquake in Kansu, China, registered 8.5 on the Richter Scale and released 32 times more energy than the one in Messina, Italy, that registered 7.5.**

7. An earthquake that registers between 8.0 and 8.9 on the Richter Scale is likely to happen *about five times* a year. **An earthquake that registers between 8.0 and 8.9 on the Richter Scale is likely to happen less than once a year.**

8. To help make your home earthquake safe, place *heavy objects* on the highest shelves. **To help make your home earthquake safe, place lightweight objects on the highest shelves.**

9. An earthquake with a magnitude of 6.7 would release 32 times more energy than an earthquake with a *magnitude of 7.7*. **An earthquake with a magnitude of 6.7 would release 32 times more energy than an earthquake with a magnitude of 5.7.**

10. In a year, you could expect *about 6000* earthquakes with magnitude between 1.0 and 3.9. **In a year, you could expect more than 100 000 earthquakes with magnitudes between 1.0 and 3.9.**

Chapter 9

STUDY GUIDE

• Living on a Fault

Use the terms in the box to complete the sentences.

seismic-safe	earthquake	magnitudes
building codes	vibrations	crumbling structures
San Francisco Bay	highways	underground pipes

1. An **earthquake** can result in the loss of life and great damage to structures built by people.

2. Most deaths occur when people are trapped in or on **crumbling structures** .

3. Much of the Pacific Coast including the **San Francisco Bay** area is earthquake-prone.

4. As a result, California has enforced strict **building codes** for new construction.

5. The codes have requirements to make new buildings **seismic-safe** structures.

6. Today many high-rise office buildings stand on steel and rubber springs that help the building ride out the **vibrations** caused by earthquakes.

7. **Highways** are being built with reinforcing rods in their cement columns.

8. Lives and property could be saved by replacing old **underground pipes** for gas and water with new ones that will bend during an earthquake.

9. By having seismic-safe structures, the San Francisco Bay area did not experience as much loss of life as other areas that had earthquakes with similar **magnitudes** .

Answer the following questions in complete sentences.

1. What do the San Francisco Bay area, Armenia, and Iran have in common? **All are sites of recent earthquakes.**

2. How are highway pillars with spiral reinforcing rods wrapped around them and buildings standing on steel and rubber springs alike? **Both are structures that are seismic-safe.**

3. Why did Interstate 880 collapse during the earthquake in the San Francisco Bay area? **The highway was not seismic-safe and could not withstand the earthquake's vibrations.**

4. Why did California enforce stricter building codes? **California is part of an earthquake-prone area. The codes are intended to help make structures seismic-safe.**

Chapter 10

STUDY GUIDE

● Volcanoes and Earth's Moving Plates

Write the term or phrase that matches each definition below. Use the letters in the boxes to answer Item 14.

1. P [L] A T E S
2.   [L] A V A
3. C [R] A T E R
4. R I [F] T S
5. A C T I V [E]
6. D O [R] M A N T
7. R I N G O [F] F I R E
8.   [V] E N T S
9. D I [V] E R G E N T
10.   M [A] G M A
11. C O N V [E] R G E N T
12.   V O L C A [N] O
13. H O T S P O [T]

1. Structures in Earth that move on the asthenosphere
2. Magma that flows out onto Earth's surface
3. Opening at the top of a volcano's vent
4. Long, deep cracks formed when plates separate
5. The state of volcanoes currently spewing smoke, ash, steam, cinders, and/or lava
6. The state of volcanoes not currently active
7. Area around Pacific Plate where earthquakes and volcanoes are common, the Pacific _____
8. Openings in Earth's crust that allow magma to reach the surface
9. Type of boundary where plates separate
10. Melted rock deep inside Earth
11. Type of boundary where one plate slides under another plate
12. Mountain formed from layers of lava and volcanic ash
13. Area in Earth's mantle hot enough to melt rock into magma and create volcanoes
14. What process helps in the formation of volcanoes? **plate movement**

Chapter 10

STUDY GUIDE

● Energy from Earth

Answer the following questions on the lines provided.

1. Define geothermal energy. Heat from magma is used to produce steam that spins generators to make electricity. _____

2. Write the following sentences in the proper sequence to show how geothermal energy from magma is used.
   - Hot water produces steam.
   - Generators make electricity.
   - Magma heats water.
   - Steam spins generators.
   - Magma is very hot.

   (1) **Magma is very hot.**
   (2) **Magma heats water.**
   (3) **Hot water produces steam.**
   (4) **Steam spins generators.**
   (5) **Generators make electricity.**

3. Make a list of the advantages and disadvantages of using geothermal energy instead of energy from fossil fuels.

   Advantages
   reductions in oil spills
   mine waste
   polluting gases
   Disadvantages
   Geothermal energy from magma is available only at certain locations.
   Geothermal energy from hot dry rock is very expensive at present.

4. What are the two main engineering problems in getting energy from hot dry rock?
   (1) drilling to great depths, (2) having to create fissures or cracks in rocks that don't already have them _____

Chapter 10
STUDY GUIDE

● Eruptions and Forms of Volcanoes

Solve the crossword puzzle by using the definitions provided as clues.

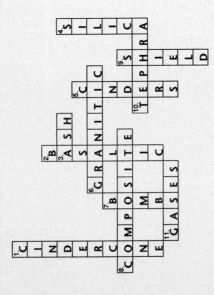

Across

3. Smallest-sized tephra
6. Type of magma containing a lot of silica and water vapor
8. Volcano made of alternating layers of lava and tephra
10. Volcanic material thrown out during eruptions
11. Substances that affect the explosiveness of volcanic eruptions

Answer the question in the space provided.

12. Two important factors determine whether an eruption will be explosive or quiet. What are they? the amount of water vapor and other gases in the magma and whether the magma is basaltic or granitic

Down

1. Steep-sided volcano made of tephra (2 words)
2. Type of magma containing little silica
4. Mineral that affects the thickness of magma
5. Medium-sized tephra
7. Larger-sized tephra
9. Broad volcano made of flat layers of basaltic lava

Chapter 10
STUDY GUIDE

● Igneous Rock Features

In the blank at the left, write the letter of the term or phrase that correctly completes each statement.

___a___ 1. Masses of magma that cool underground and form the largest igneous rock bodies are called _____.
    a. batholiths   b. laccoliths

___b___ 2. Ship Rock in New Mexico is an example of a _____.
    a. laccolith   b. volcanic neck

___a___ 3. Most igneous activity takes place _____.
    a. underground   b. above ground

___b___ 4. Magma that squeezes into a horizontal crack and hardens forms a _____.
    a. dike   b. sill

___b___ 5. When the top of a volcano collapses into the vent, a _____ is formed.
    a. crater   b. caldera

___b___ 6. A dome of rock pushed up by a magma sill is a _____.
    a. batholith   b. laccolith

___a___ 7. Volcanic features that can sometimes be seen above ground are _____.
    a. volcanic necks and batholiths   b. dikes and sills

___a___ 8. Magma that squeezes into a vertical crack and hardens forms a _____.
    a. dike   b. sill

___b___ 9. Crater Lake in Oregon is an example of a _____.
    a. dike   b. caldera

___b___ 10. When erosion wears away the outside of a volcano, sometimes a solid magma core called a _____ is left exposed.
    a. cinder cone   b. volcanic neck

___a___ 11. The granite domes in Yosemite National Park in California are part of a _____.
    a. batholith   b. sill

___b___ 12. Volcanoes are examples of igneous activity _____.
    a. underground   b. above ground

___b___ 13. Magma that cools underground forms _____ igneous rock.
    a. extrusive   b. intrusive

___a___ 14. The difference between dikes and sills is the _____ of their formation.
    a. direction   b. size

Chapter 11

STUDY GUIDE

● Continental Drift

Use the words and phrases in the boxes to complete each part of the outline.

Climate clues	Plants
Fossil clues	Rock clues
Glaciers	

Evidence for continental drift

I. Early evidence

A. Puzzlelike fit of continents

B. **Fossil clues**

  1. *Mesosaurus* _____

  2. *Glossopteris* _____

  3. **Plants** _____

C. **Climate clues**

  1. **Glaciers** _____

  2. Glacial deposits _____

D. **Rock clues** _____

Magnetic evidence	Reversal of magnetic alignment of rocks
Age evidence	Ocean rock younger than continental rock
Older rock farther from mid-ocean ridge	

II. Later evidence: seafloor spreading

A. **Age evidence**

  1. *Glomar Challenger* research

    a. Newer rock near mid-ocean ridge _____

    b. **Older rock farther from mid-ocean ridge** _____

    c. **Ocean rock younger than continental rock** _____

B. **Magnetic evidence**

  1. Known reversal of Earth's magnetic field _____

  2. **Reversal of magnetic alignment of rocks** _____

Chapter 11

STUDY GUIDE

● Seafloor Spreading

Use words in the boxes to fill in the blanks.

inner core	liquid	rock
iron and nickel	outer core	solid

Scientists know Earth's interior is made mostly of layers of **rock** _____.

Some layers, like the center part, called the **inner core** _____ are hard and **solid** _____. Other layers are not. The layer next to the center, called the **outer core** _____, is **liquid** _____. Both parts of the core are made of **iron and nickel** _____.

continents	mantle	plasticlike
crust	oceans	soil
hot		

The largest layer inside Earth is called the **mantle** _____. It's neither completely solid nor completely liquid, but **plasticlike** _____. It's extremely **hot** _____.

Earth's outermost layer is the **crust** _____. This layer is about 5 km thick under the **oceans** _____ and up to 35 km thick under the **continents** _____. On top of the outer layer is the weathered rock we call **soil** _____.

Chapter 11
STUDY GUIDE ● **Theory of Plate Tectonics**

Text Pages 304–313

In the blank at the left, write the letter of the term or phrase that best completes each statement.

b ___ 1. The theory that Earth's crust and upper mantle are broken into sections is called _____ .
   a. seafloor spreading   b. plate tectonics

a ___ 2. Plates are composed of the _____ .
   a. crust and part of the upper mantle   b. lithosphere and asthenosphere

b ___ 3. The lithosphere is composed of the _____ .
   a. plates and seafloor   b. crust and upper mantle

a ___ 4. Plates float on the _____ .
   a. asthenosphere   b. lithosphere

a ___ 5. Plates can _____ .
   a. pull apart, collide, and move past one another   b. erupt and form precipitation

b ___ 6. The boundary between two plates that are moving apart is a _____ boundary.
   a. convergent   b. divergent

a ___ 7. When ocean plates collide with continental plates, the denser ocean plate _____ .
   a. sinks   b. rises

b ___ 8. The area where a plate descends is a _____ .
   a. convergent boundary   b. subduction zone

b ___ 9. A _____ is created where one plate moves under another.
   a. mantle   b. trench

a ___ 10. A subducted plate melts, forming _____ .
   a. magma and volcanic mountains   b. the lithosphere

b ___ 11. Two continental plates may collide and cause _____ .
   a. glaciers   b. earthquakes

a ___ 12. Scientists think plates are moved by _____ .
   a. convection currents   b. volcanoes

b ___ 13. A place where plates slide past one another is a _____ .
   a. divergent fault   b. transform fault

b ___ 14. The San Andreas Fault is a _____ .
   a. volcano   b. transform fault

a ___ 15. The Himalayas were formed at a _____ .
   a. convergent boundary   b. transform fault

Chapter 11
STUDY GUIDE ● **Before Pangaea, Rodinia**

Text Pages 314–315

Complete each statement from your textbook on the lines provided.

1. Edges of some continents look as if they would **fit together** .

2. People wondered if these continents had been **joined together at one time** .

3. In 1915, Alfred Wegener proposed an idea called **continental drift** .

4. This idea states that continents moved through the **seafloor to their present locations** .

5. Wegener thought that long ago the continents formed **one landmass** .

6. He named it Pangaea, which means **all land** .

7. Wegener's idea was rejected. The idea was so different that **most people closed their minds to it** .

8. Today Wegener's ideas about continental drift are **accepted by most scientists** .

9. Today some people still have trouble **accepting new ideas** .

10. One new idea that is still being debated explains **how the dinosaurs died** .

11. Walter and Luis Alvarez think that a large rocky object **collided with Earth** .

12. This collision threw **tons of dust into the air** .

13. The dust blocked the **sunlight** .

14. This caused **the death of the dinosaurs** .

Answer the questions on the lines provided.

15. Explain how Pangaea fits into Wegener's theory of continental drift. **Pangaea is the huge landmass that existed before the continents broke apart and drifted to their current locations.**

16. State one reason why Wegener's ideas about continental drift were not believed. **Wegener couldn't explain how, when, or why continental drift occurred.**

Chapter 12
STUDY GUIDE ● Fossils

Match the terms in Column I with their descriptions in Column II. Write the letter of the correct phrase in the blank at the left.

Column I

c 1. fossil

f 2. cast

e 3. mold

a 4. index fossil

b 5. carbonaceous film

d 6. petrified remain

Column II

a. Fossil from a species that existed on Earth for a short period of time

b. Fossil made from a thin film of carbon atoms and molecules

c. Remain, imprint, or trace of a once-living organism

d. Hard and rocklike fossil

e. Cavity left in rock by a decayed organism

f. Produced when a cavity is filled with solid matter

Circle the word in the blank that makes the statement correct.

7. (Impressions / **Fossils**) are preserved remains or traces of life-forms.

8. Organisms have a better chance of being preserved if they have (**hard** / soft) parts.

9. A hard, rocklike fossil, called a (**petrified** / trace) fossil develops when minerals fill spaces left when the original substance dissolves.

10. A carbonaceous (decay / **film**) fossil is made when pressure and heat force out gases and liquids, leaving a thin residue of the organism.

11. A (mold / **cast**) is made when sediments fill in a cavity and harden.

12. (**Original** / Carbon) remains have been preserved in frozen ground and in amber.

13. Preserved tracks and other evidence of animal activity are called (index / **trace**) fossils.

14. Fossils of life-forms that existed on Earth for a short period of time and were widespread geographically are called (**index** / trace) fossils.

15. Fossils show that the (**environment** / elevation) of Antarctica has changed greatly.

Chapter 12
STUDY GUIDE ● Extinction of Dinosaurs

Use the words in the boxes to fill in the blanks.

| dominant | mammals | 160 million | intelligent |

Dinosaurs were abundant on Earth's land for about **160 million** years. These fast, agile, and **intelligent** animals were the **dominant** land animals. Only after the end of their rule did another class of animals, **mammals**, increase.

| Alvarez, iridium, collision | dinosaurs, dust, theory | extinct, meteorite | western, 66 million |

The remains of **dinosaurs** have been found in the **western** part of the United States. These great animals have been **extinct** for about **66 million** years. Two scientists, Luis **Alvarez** and Walter **Alvarez**, have uncovered traces of **iridium** in rock layers. They now think they know why the animals died. Their **theory** is that Earth and a **meteorite** from space had a **collision**. This raised **dust**, which dimmed the sun's light. The meteorite's impact would also account for the iridium deposit.

| mineral | photosynthesis | temperature | volcanic activity |

The meteorite collision has been rejected by some scientists who think increased **volcanic activity** is a more likely theory. Either event would explain the presence of the rare **mineral** iridium and would have resulted in a dimming of the sun. This would kill plants that depend on the sun for **photosynthesis** and would lower Earth's **temperature**.

Chapter 12

STUDY GUIDE • Relative Ages of Rocks

In the blank at the left, write the letter of the term or phrase that best completes each statement.

b 1. In layers of undisturbed sedimentary rock, the oldest rocks are on the _____.
   a. top   b. bottom

a 2. Sediments deposited in layers form _____ rocks.
   a. sedimentary   b. igneous

a 3. The statement that old rocks are on the bottom in layers of undisturbed rock is called the _____.
   a. principle of superposition   b. tectonic theory

b 4. Sometimes layers of rock are overturned by forces generated by _____.
   a. superposition   b. tectonic activity

a 5. Determining the age of rocks by examining their position in a layer is called _____.
   a. relative dating   b. faulting

b 6. Gaps in rock layers are called _____.
   a. faults   b. unconformities

b 7. The type of unconformity in which an erosional surface exists in one of several horizontal layers is called a(n) _____.
   a. angular unconformity   b. disconformity

b 8. Matching of rock layers in two different areas is called _____ the layers.
   a. concluding   b. correlating

a 9. One way to match rock layers that are apart is to see if the same type of _____ are found in both places.
   a. fossils   b. water

b 10. Sometimes rock layers are visible because they have been exposed by _____ cutting through them.
   a. volcanoes   b. streams

a 11. Some unconformities are the result of _____.
   a. erosion   b. volcanoes

12. Number the rock layers according to their relative ages. Label the oldest rock type #1.

A. #6
B. #5
C. #3
D. #2
E. #1
F. #4

Chapter 12

STUDY GUIDE • Absolute Ages of Rocks

Use the words in the boxes to fill in the blanks.

absolute dating	element	neutrons
age	isotopes	radioactive
atoms	lead-206	uranium-238

Besides relative dating, geologists use another method to determine in years the **age** of rocks and other objects. It's called **absolute dating** in objects.

It's a process that uses the properties of the **atoms** .

Elements can have atoms with different numbers of **neutrons** in their nuclei.

Some of these **isotopes** undergo a process of **radioactive** decay. When the isotope decays, a new **element** is formed. An example of this decay is the change of the isotope **uranium-238** to **lead-206** .

carbon-14	radiometric dating
daughter product	uniformitarianism
half-life	
nitrogen-14	
parent material	

Another example of decaying isotopes is the isotope **carbon-14** , which decays to **nitrogen-14** . The original isotope in this process is called the **parent material** . The isotope that results from the decay is the **daughter product** .

Every radioactive **parent material** has a certain rate at which it decays to its **daughter product** . This rate is known as its **half-life** .

Calculating the absolute age of a rock is called **radiometric dating** . Long before this was possible, a Scottish scientist estimated that Earth was millions of years old. He used the principle called **uniformitarianism** , which states that Earth's processes occurring today are similar to those that occurred in the past.

Chapter 13

STUDY GUIDE

● Evolution and Geologic Time

Use the words in the box to fill in the blanks in the statements.

adapted	continents	environment	extinct
epochs	eras	fossils	plate tectonics
geologic time scale	natural selection	organic evolution	periods
species			

1. The division of Earth's history into units makes up the **geologic time scale**.

2. Major divisions of Earth's history are **eras**.

3. Each major division may be divided into **periods**.

4. The Cenozoic Era is divided into **epochs**.

5. Clues to which organisms lived in different eras are found in **fossils**.

6. A gradual change in life-forms over time is **organic evolution**.

7. Each change in Earth created different surroundings for organisms, these surroundings are called their **environment**.

8. A group of organisms that normally reproduce only among themselves is a **species**.

9. After major changes in Earth's environments, species either died out or **adapted**.

10. Species that could not adapt to changes eventually became **extinct**.

11. Organisms with traits that are suited to an environment survive by the process of **natural selection**.

12. At different times in Earth's history, plate tectonics caused collision and separation of **continents**.

13. Many species adapted or became extinct because **plate tectonics** caused their environments to change when the continents collided or separated.

Chapter 13

STUDY GUIDE

● Present-Day Rapid Extinctions

Read each statement, and then answer the questions in complete sentences.

1. Throughout Earth's history species have become extinct. What causes extinction? **Changes in environments or competition with other species for resources cause extinction.**

2. The activities of humans living about 10 000 years ago may have caused some extinctions. How do present-day humans affect animal species? **They are causing extinctions at a greater rate.**

3. How might economic development in a city or suburb affect the habitat of birds that are in the area? **Trees are often cut down to make room for buildings and factories, making conditions more difficult for birds.**

4. Tropical rain forests contain 50 to 80 percent of Earth's species. What has been done to threaten these species? **People have cleared much of these forests for farming, logging, and other industries.**

5. Organisms need a place to live, grow, and interact with each other and their environment. What is such a place called? **Such a place is called a habitat.**

6. Habitats are being destroyed in many places. What may happen to the organisms that live in these habitats? **They may become extinct.**

7. Some species that still exist are endangered. What does *endangered* mean? **A species is endangered when only a small number of its members are living.**

8. Some people want to save habitats by restricting construction and planning projects so habitats are disturbed as little as possible. What are these people trying to slow down? **They are trying to slow down the rate of extinctions.**

9. Some medicines and other products come from various organisms. Why might this be a reason to try to save organisms? **If we don't, we may miss opportunities to invent new medicines that could be derived from the organisms.**

Chapter 13
STUDY GUIDE

Early Earth History

Answer the questions on the lines at the left.

Precambrian time 1. Which era or "time" in the geologic time scale lasted the longest?

Precambrian time 2. Which era or "time" is the oldest?

cyanobacteria 3. What is thought to be one of the earliest forms of life on Earth?

oxygen; ozone layer 4. What appeared in the atmosphere that allowed more complex organisms to develop?

Invertebrates 5. What kind of animals developed near the end of the first era?

Paleozoic Era 6. What name was given to the second of Earth's eras?

warm, shallow seas 7. What covered most of Earth's surface at the beginning of the second era?

fish 8. What familiar marine life-form evolved during this era?

amphibians 9. What type of animal evolved that lived out of water but reproduced in water?

Appalachian Mountains 10. What mountain chain was caused by the collision of the Eurasian or African continental plates with the North American Plate?

reptiles 11. What type of animal is thought to have developed after the evolution of an egg that would not dry out on land?

coal 12. The formation of swamps and the decay of swamp vegetation are the basis for what fossil fuel?

Answer the following questions in complete sentences on the lines provided.

13. What happened to all of the continental plates near the end of the Paleozoic Era? **They came together to form Pangaea.**

14. What happened to many land and sea animals at this time? **The land and sea animals became extinct.**

Chapter 13
STUDY GUIDE

Middle and Recent Earth History

Determine whether each of the following statements is true or false. Write "true" in the blank at the left if the statement is true. For each false statement, write a word or phrase to replace the italicized word or phrase to make the statement true.

true 1. The first dinosaurs appeared in the *Triassic* Period.

true 2. By the *Jurassic* Period, large dinosaurs lived on Earth.

Mesozoic 3. The word *Laurasia* refers to the era of middle life.

separate 4. In this era, Pangaea began to *come together*.

true 5. Some dinosaurs ate *meat*.

true 6. One part of Pangaea was *Gondwanaland*.

true 7. Modern-day reptiles are *cold-blooded*.

true 8. It's now believed that dinosaurs may have been *warm-blooded*.

true 9. An *Archeopteryx* was similar to both dinosaurs and birds.

mammal 10. A warm-blooded vertebrate that has hair or fur and that produces milk to feed its young is a *reptile*.

true 11. At the end of the Mesozoic Era, volcanoes were very *active*.

gymnosperm 12. A plant with naked seeds is a(n) *angiosperm*.

true 13. A plant producing seeds with hard outer coverings is a(n) *angiosperm*.

true 14. The *Cenozoic Era* is the era of recent life.

became extinct 15. The Cenozoic Era began when dinosaurs *grew to be large*.

larger 16. Early species of mammals evolved into *smaller* life-forms.

true 17. Life-forms became isolated when the continents began to *break up*.

humans 18. About 10 000 years ago, *dinosaurs* became a dominant land animal.

true 19. Early *humans* may have caused the extinction of some other animals.

Australian 20. Many *North American* mammals are marsupials.

Chapter 14

STUDY GUIDE

● Earth's Atmosphere

In the blank at the left, write the letter of the term in Column II that matches each definition in Column I.

Column I

Column II

h 1. Layer of atmosphere where weather, clouds, and smog occur

a 2. Force of air determined by temperature and distance above sea level

d 3. Naturally occurring gas in the stratosphere that is considered a pollutant in the lower atmosphere

b 4. Layer of the thermosphere that has a high concentration of electrically charged particles

c 5. Most common gas in the atmosphere

f 6. Layer of atmosphere that includes the ozone layer

e 7. Type of pollution that can be formed by car exhaust and burning coal or oil

g 8. Layer of atmosphere between the thermosphere and space

a. air pressure
b. ionosphere
c. nitrogen
d. ozone
e. smog
f. stratosphere
g. exosphere
h. troposphere

In the blank, write the term that correctly completes each sentence. Use the information in your textbook.

Water vapor 9. _____ makes up from 0 to 4 percent of the atmosphere.

10. The **troposphere** contains 75 percent of the atmospheric gases.

11. The division of Earth's atmosphere into layers is based on **temperature** differences.

12. Cold air is denser than warm air and, therefore, has higher **pressure**

Water 13. _____ is the only substance that exists as a solid, liquid, and gas in Earth's atmosphere.

Identify the five main layers of Earth's atmosphere.

E _____

D _____

Atmosphere C _____

B _____

A _____

Earth

14. A is the **troposphere** .

15. B is the **stratosphere** .

16. C is the **mesosphere** .

17. D is the **thermosphere** .

18. E is the **exosphere** .

Chapter 14

STUDY GUIDE

● The Ozone Layer

Choose the correct term in the box and write each term after its definition.

| chlorofluorocarbons | ozone layer | ultraviolet radiation |

1. Layer in the stratosphere containing ozone, which absorbs ultraviolet radiation
   ozone layer

2. Type of energy from the sun that can be harmful in large amounts
   ultraviolet radiation

3. Chemicals used in some aerosol sprays, refrigerants, and some foam products
   chlorofluorocarbons

Determine whether each of the following statements is true or false. Write the word "true" or "false" in the blank. If the statement is false, rewrite it so that it's true.

false 4. The kind of oxygen we breathe can absorb ultraviolet radiation.
   The kind of oxygen we breathe can't absorb ultraviolet radiation.

true 5. If the ozone layer disappeared, cancer rates would be much higher than they are now.

false 6. Chlorofluorocarbons are making the ozone layer thicker.
   Chlorofluorocarbons are making the ozone layer thinner.

true 7. The ozone layer acts as a shield between us and ultraviolet radiation.

false 8. A thick, unchanging layer of ozone covers the entire Earth.
   The ozone layer is thinning and developing holes. These holes appear during certain seasons and disappear during others.

false 9. Ozone molecules destroy chlorofluorocarbon molecules.
   Chlorofluorocarbon molecules destroy ozone molecules.

NAME DATE CLASS

Chapter 14

STUDY GUIDE

Text Pages 402–409

Energy from the Sun

Use the words in the box to fill in the blanks.

heat	life	absorb	radiation
sun	lower	reflects	density
waves	current	contact	conduction
sinks	campfire	environment	temperature
space	surfaces	atmosphere	convection

The **sun** is the source of all energy in our atmosphere. When Earth receives this energy, some energy escapes back into **space**, some is absorbed by the **atmosphere**, and some is absorbed by land and water **surfaces**. The balance among these three help the atmosphere support **life**. Energy reaches Earth in the form of radiant energy, or **radiation**. This process is the transfer of energy by **waves**. You experience radiation when you sit by a **campfire** and your skin becomes warm. The molecules of your skin **absorb** the energy and you feel **heat**. Heat is the transfer of energy from an object with a higher **temperature** to an object with a **lower** temperature. Some radiation isn't absorbed by the atmosphere or surface objects; it **reflects** off the atmosphere or surface.

Conduction is the transfer of energy that occurs when molecules bump into one another and heat is transferred through direct **contact**. **Convection** is the transfer of heat that occurs because of **density** differences in the air. Because cold air has a higher density than warm air, cold air **sinks**—this pushes up the warm air. This rise and fall of air sets up a circular movement called a convection **current**. Convection currents and other processes that transfer energy help provide the **environment** we live in.

NAME DATE CLASS

Chapter 14

STUDY GUIDE

Text Pages 410–419

Movement of Air

Use the diagrams below to identify the following terms: doldrums, land breeze, polar easterlies, prevailing westerlies, trade winds, sea breeze. Write each term next to the appropriate number.

1. **polar easterlies**
2. **prevailing westerlies**
3. **trade winds**
4. **doldrums**
5. **trade winds**
6. **prevailing westerlies**
7. **polar easterlies**

FIGURE 1

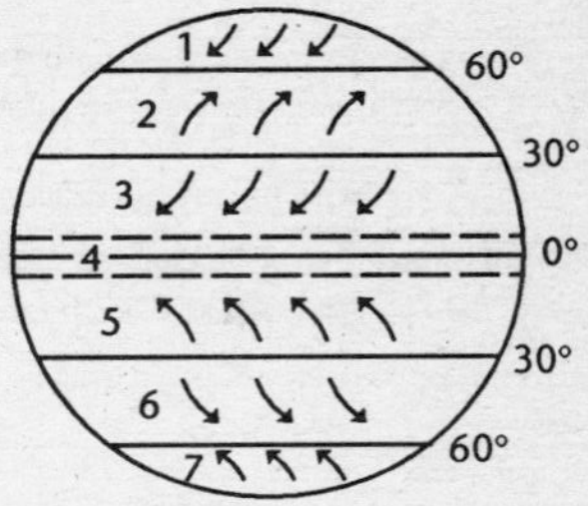

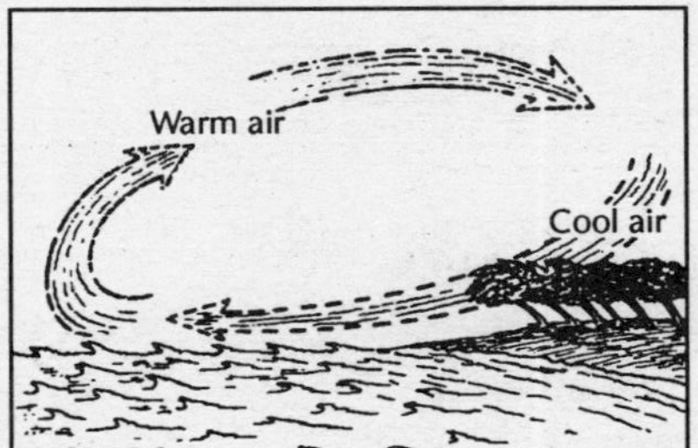

FIGURE 2

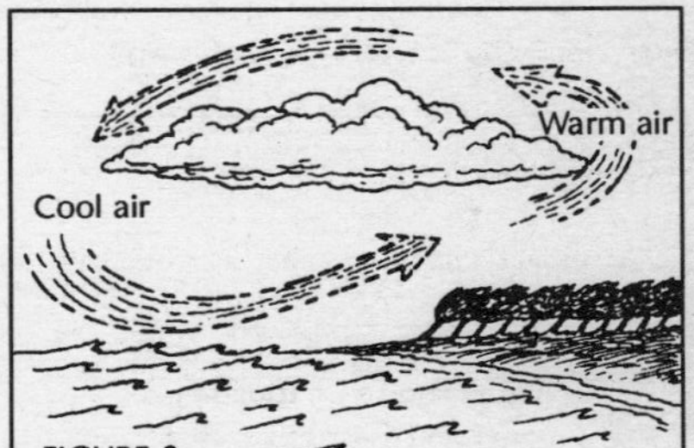

FIGURE 3

8. **land breeze**
9. **sea breeze**

In the blank on the left, write the term that matches each definition.

Coriolis effect 10. The turning of air masses from their original paths because of Earth's rotation

jet streams 11. High altitude winds that occur in places where trade winds and polar easterlies meet prevailing westerlies

wind systems 12. Air movement patterns on Earth's surface as shown in Figure 1

convection current 13. Circular movement of air that causes the winds shown in Figure 2

Chapter 15

STUDY GUIDE

● Weather Patterns

Fill in the sentence outline using information from Section 15-2 in your textbook.

I. Changes in Weather

A. An air mass is <u>a large body of air that has the same properties as the surface over which it develops.</u>

B. A front is <u>the boundary formed when two air masses collide.</u>

  1. A warm front develops when <u>a warm air mass meets a cold air mass and slides up over it.</u>

  2. A cold front forms when <u>a cold air mass invades a warm air mass and forces the warm air up rapidly.</u>

  3. A stationary front forms when <u>a warm or cold front stops moving and remains in the same place for several days.</u>

  4. An occluded front results when <u>two cool air masses merge, forcing the warmer air between them to rise.</u>

II. Pressure Systems

A. High pressure systems generally mean clear weather because <u>as cold air sinks, it warms and its water vapor evaporates, so there is no moisture to form clouds.</u>

B. Low pressure systems generally mean cloudy weather because <u>warm, moist air rises, cools, condenses, and forms clouds.</u>

III. Severe Weather

A. Thunderstorms result from <u>the rapid upward movement of warm, moist air which cools, condenses, and forms high clouds.</u>

B. Tornadoes occur in thunderstorms when <u>the wind at different heights blows in different directions and at different speeds. A strong updraft tilts these winds and produces rotation inside the thunderstorm. A funnel cloud appears.</u>

C. Hurricanes are <u>large, swirling low pressure systems that form over tropical oceans when opposing winds meet and begin to rotate over warm water.</u>

Chapter 15

STUDY GUIDE

● What Is Weather?

In the word search puzzle, find and circle the word that completes each sentence. Write the word on the line.

1. The present state of the atmosphere is the <u>weather</u>.

2. <u>Humidity</u> is the amount of water vapor in the air.

3. Air is <u>saturated</u> when it is holding all the moisture it can at a certain temperature.

4. The temperature at which air is saturated and condensation begins is the <u>dew</u> point.

5. <u>Relative</u> humidity is the amount of water vapor in air compared to the amount of water vapor air can hold at a certain temperature.

6. A <u>psychrometer</u> is an instrument that measures relative humidity.

7. When millions of tiny drops of water around dust particles form from condensed humid air, a <u>cloud</u> forms.

8. A stratus cloud that forms near the ground is <u>fog</u>.

9. Water droplets that become too heavy to remain suspended in the air fall out of the clouds as <u>precipitation</u>.

10. <u>Hail</u> forms when water drops freeze in layers around small nuclei of ice.

11. Water drops that fall when the temperature is above freezing fall as <u>rain</u>.

12. Water drops that fall when the temperature is below freezing fall as <u>snow</u>.

13. When snow passes through warm air, melts, and refreezes near the ground, it becomes <u>sleet</u>.

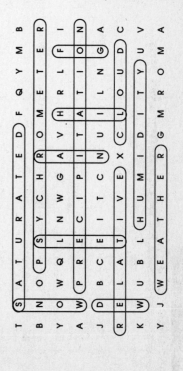

```
T  S  A  T  U  R  A  T  E  D  F  Q  Y  M  B
B  N  O  P  S  Y  C  H  R  O  M  E  T  E  R
Y  O  W  Q  L  N  W  G  A  V  H  R  L  F  I
A  W  P  R  E  C  I  P  I  T  A  T  I  O  N
J  D  B  C  E  I  T  C  N  U  I  L  N  G  A
R  E  L  A  T  I  V  E  X  C  L  O  U  D  C
K  U  B  L  H  U  M  I  D  I  T  Y  U  V  V
Y  J  W  E  A  T  H  E  R  G  M  R  O  M  A
```

STUDY GUIDE

● Forecasting Weather

Text Pages 440–443

In the blank at the left, write the letter of the term in Column II that matches each definition in Column I.

Column I

l ___ 1. Advisory to prepare for severe weather

b ___ 2. Person who studies the weather

a ___ 3. Average of all weather conditions of an area over a long period

e ___ 4. Weather information at a specific location

d ___ 5. Line connecting points of equal temperature on a weather map

f ___ 6. Regions on Earth that have cold winters, hot summers, and mild springs and falls

j ___ 7. Advisory that severe weather conditions exist

h ___ 8. Regions on Earth that have hot temperatures all year

c ___ 9. Line connecting points of equal atmospheric pressure on a weather map

g ___ 10. Regions on Earth extending from the poles to 66 1/2° north and south latitudes

Column II

a. climate

b. meteorologist

c. isobar

d. isotherm

e. station model

f. temperate zones

g. polar zones

h. tropical zones

i. watch

j. warning

Answer the following questions on the lines provided.

11. What do you do if a watch is issued? If a warning is issued? With a watch, you prepare for bad weather and make plans for where you will go if conditions get worse. With a warning, severe weather exists in your area and you should take immediate action by taking shelter or going to high ground.

12. How do meteorologists gather weather information? They measure temperature, air pressure, wind speed and direction, humidity, and precipitation. They include data gathered by radar, computers, balloons, and weather satellites.

13. What can isobars tell you about wind speed? Isobars that are close together on a weather map mean that there are great pressure differences in a small area and the winds will be strong. Isobars that are farther apart mean that there is less difference in pressure and the winds will be gentler.

STUDY GUIDE

● Changing the Weather

Text Pages 444–459

Answer the questions below on the lines provided.

1. List several human activities that alter the weather. Planting trees; mulching around plants or irrigating soil; releasing smoke, other particles, and gases into the atmosphere; building cities; cutting forests; making artificial lakes.

2. Why is the air over cities usually warmer than the air over rural areas? Buildings and other structures in cities retain heat that is gradually released into the atmosphere.

3. What are the two main conditions that some scientists hypothesize are needed for successful cloud seeding? Water vapor must be present, and the air temperature must be near the dew point.

4. Why have many cloud seeding experiments failed? Conditions that affect weather vary so much from place to place and from day to day.

5. What are two methods used for cloud seeding? Particles are either shot into clouds from the ground or dropped into clouds from airplanes.

6. What is the potential danger in seeding clouds to reduce hurricane wind speeds? Some scientists fear that cloud seeding could make hurricanes stronger.

7. At what size does a particle and its added ice crystals fall from a cloud as precipitation? When its diameter reaches 0.2 millimeters

8. What are three examples of when cloud seeding experiments have been successful? clearing fog at airports; increasing snowfall in some mountain resorts; increasing rainfall in some areas affected by drought

STUDY GUIDE • What Is Climate?

Determine whether each statement below is true or false. Write "true" in the blank at the left if the statement is true. For each false statement, write a word or phrase to replace the italicized word or phrase to make the statement true.

true 1. *Tropical* regions receive the most solar radiation.

slower 2. Water heats up and cools down *faster* than land.

true 3. Winds blowing from the sea contain *more* moisture than winds blowing from the land.

higher 4. Temperatures in a large city are generally *lower* than temperatures in the surrounding rural areas.

fewer 5. There are *more* air molecules to absorb heat emitted by Earth's surface at *higher* elevations than at sea level.

away from 6. Deserts are common on the side of a mountain *facing* the wind.

the tropics 7. Year-round temperatures in *temperate zones* are always hot, except at high elevations.

true 8. As air rises, it cools down.

Answer the following questions on the lines provided.

9. What are three weather conditions that are considered in determining a region's climate? **Answers should include temperature, precipitation, air pressure, humidity, or days of sunshine.**

10. What are four factors that affect the climate of a region? **Answers should include latitude, topography, locations of lakes and oceans, availability of moisture, global wind patterns, ocean currents, or location of air masses.**

STUDY GUIDE • Climate Types

Use the terms in the box to complete the sentences.

climatologists	vegetation	wet	behavioral
ferns	semiarid	hibernation	
adaptations	continental	estivation	

1. Some mammals undergo a period of inactivity in winter called __hibernation__.

2. Changes in activity that help organisms survive in a certain environment are __behavioral__ adaptations.

3. Dry climates are divided into __semiarid__ and arid.

4. Where there is heavy rainfall, some typical plants are moss-draped trees and __ferns__.

5. People who study climates are called __climatologists__.

6. __Estivation__ is an inactive state through which lungfish survive periods of intense heat.

7. Most __wet__ climates are found between latitudes 30° north and 30° south.

8. Characteristics that organisms develop over a long time that help them survive are called __adaptations__.

9. One of the six climate groups in the Köppen Climate Classification System is the __continental__ climate.

10. The type of __vegetation__ in a region depends on the climate.

Complete the following item on the lines provided.

11. List the six climate groups in the Köppen Climate Classification System.

tropical

dry

mild

continental

polar

high elevation

STUDY GUIDE

• Climatic Changes

Text Pages 462–469

In the blank, write the letter of the term or phrase that best completes each statement.

___a___ 1. The farther from the equator, the _____ the hours of daylight vary during the year.
    a. more   b. less

___b___ 2. El Niño affects the world's weather _____.
    a. during the summer months   b. for a period of time longer than three months

___a___ 3. Catastrophic events that have affected Earth's climate in the past include _____.
    a. volcanic eruptions   b. glaciation

___b___ 4. Ice sheets formed when the temperature of Earth was higher have _____ concentrations of carbon dioxide.
    a. smaller   b. greater

___b___ 5. _____ causes the seasons.
    a. a change in Earth's orbit   b. the tilt of Earth's axis

Answer the following questions on the lines provided.

6. What are some of the major kinds of evidence that Earth's climate differed in the past? Fossils of plants and animals from different parts of Earth; glacial erosion and deposition around the world; thickness of tree rings.

7. How do meteorite impacts affect Earth's climate? They release into the atmosphere large amounts of dust, ash, and smoke that block solar radiation.

8. Why might the movement of the plates in Earth's crust affect the climate? These plate movements affect the transfer of heat on Earth's surface, which affects winds and precipitation.

9. How did the eruption of Mount Pinatubo in 1991 affect Earth's climate? Its volcanic ash cooled temperatures worldwide.

10. What effects would an increase in clouds have on Earth's climate? More clouds might cause more heat to be retained in Earth's atmosphere—the greenhouse effect. Or they might block more incoming solar radiation, which would have a cooling effect.

STUDY GUIDE

• How Can Global Warming Be Slowed?

Text Pages 470–475

Match the words in Column I with the phrases in Column II. Write the letter of the correct phrase in the blank on the left.

Column I

___f___ 1. fossil fuels

___c___ 2. deforestation

___d___ 3. burning

___a___ 4. plants

___b___ 5. giant screen

___e___ 6. nitrous oxide

Column II

a. remove carbon dioxide from atmosphere

b. possible way to reduce global warming

c. mass removal of trees

d. adds carbon dioxide to atmosphere

e. gas that contributes to global warming

f. petroleum, natural gas, and coal

Answer the following questions on the lines provided.

7. What are some of the ways that people can reduce their use of fossil fuels? They can reduce activities that burn fuels, such as heating and cooling homes, watching television, taking car rides, and so on. Also, they can develop other sources of energy that do not burn fossil fuels, such as solar, wind, geothermal, and so forth. They can also use passive solar means to heat and cool homes.

8. What are examples of reasons why forests are being cleared in different parts of the world? for mining, roads, farming, building, cattle grazing, and oil drilling

9. How can planting vegetation help reduce global warming? Plants remove carbon dioxide from the atmosphere. In addition, plants and trees can provide wind cover and shade and thus reduce the use of electricity for warming and cooling homes.

10. Why have some scientists suggested that billions of aluminum balloons should be released into the atmosphere? as a possible way of reflecting solar radiation and reducing global warming

Chapter 17
STUDY GUIDE • Ocean Water

Use the words in the box to complete the statements.

volcanoes	iron
halite	chlorine
basins	salinity

1. Billions of years ago, low areas on Earth called **basins** _____ filled with water to form oceans.

2. Besides sodium, **chlorine** _____ is the most abundant element in seawater.

3. The **salinity** _____ of seawater is a measure of the amount of solids dissolved in it.

4. Scientists hypothesize that water vapor from **volcanoes** _____ accumulated in Earth's early atmosphere and caused torrential rains to fall.

5. The salt used to flavor food is called **halite** _____.

6. One example of an element that forms a solid and falls to the ocean floor is **iron** _____.

Answer the following questions on the lines provided.

7. Where do the salts that are dissolved in seawater come from? **Rivers and groundwater dissolve the salts when they flow through rock and minerals and then transport them to the oceans.**

8. How do living things affect the amount of calcium and silica in the oceans? **Sea animals use these substances in their life processes, including the formation of bones and shells.**

9. How do volcanoes affect the composition of the oceans? **They add sulfur and chlorine gas.**

10. What are some of the ways in which oceans affect life on land? **Students may say that oceans influence the weather, are a source of food, and act as both a means of transportation and a barrier between landmasses.**

Chapter 17
STUDY GUIDE • Ocean Currents

Write answers on the lines provided.

1. What currents are influenced by the Coriolis effect? **surface currents**

2. Where surface currents carry water away from an area, an upwelling may occur. What is it that "wells up"? What does it carry with it? **Cold water wells up. It brings up nutrients from deep in the ocean.**

3. Is the Gulf Stream a surface current or a density current? **It is a surface current.**

4. What kind of water movement helps the fishing industry? How? **Upwelling brings nutrients that attract fish.**

5. Explain how understanding the Gulf Stream helped eighteenth century sailing ships travel more rapidly from America to England. **Ships sailed on the Gulf Stream when sailing east so that this current (which flows east) could carry them quickly.**

6. Which coasts of continents tend to be warmer, the eastern or the western? Explain. **Eastern coasts tend to be warmer because the eastern coasts are affected by warm ocean currents.**

7. On the map below, draw an arrow to represent the Gulf Stream and label it.

8. On the map, draw an arrow representing the South Equatorial Current west of South America and label it.

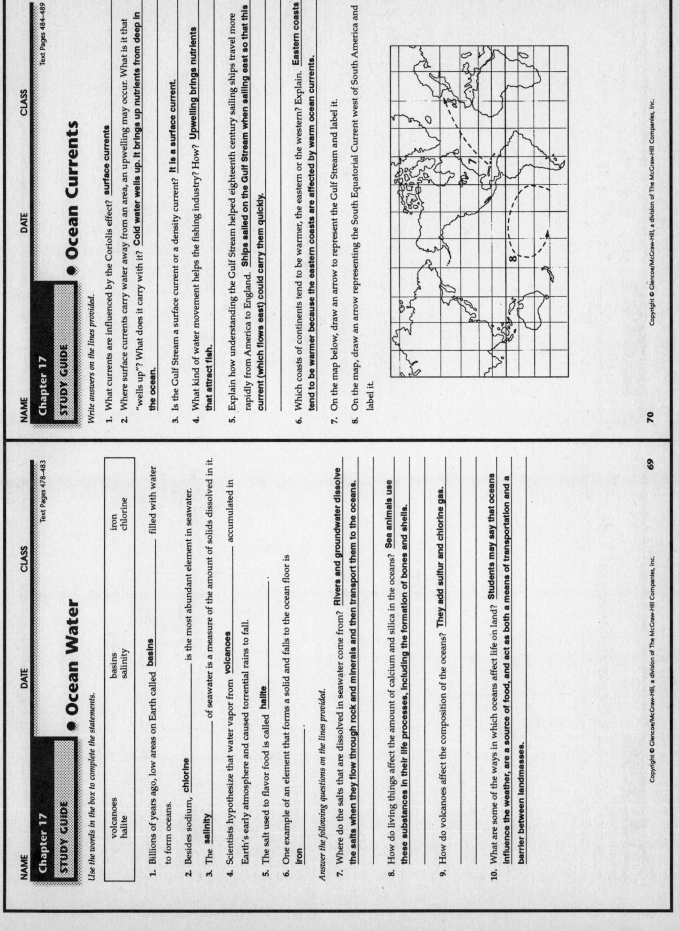

STUDY GUIDE

● Tapping Tidal Energy

Answer the following questions on the lines provided.

1. Where is a tidal power plant planned? the Bay of Fundy in Nova Scotia, Canada
   _____

2. Average tidal ranges throughout the world are between 0.5 and 3 meters. Explain why the Bay of
   Fundy is a better than average place to build a tidal power plant. **Tidal range in the Bay of Fundy**
   reaches 16 meters, the greatest on Earth. Therefore the outgoing tide would have great energy.

3. What would hold back the water after the Bay of Fundy tide has come in? **Dam gates would be**
   closed.
   _____

4. What would the outgoing water pass over as it leaves the dam? **It would pass over turbines.**
   _____

5. How would the Bay of Fundy power plant produce electricity? **Kinetic energy from falling water**
   could be used to turn turbines. Turbines could generate electricity.

6. List advantages of the Bay of Fundy power plant. **The plant would not pollute, would produce a**
   great supply of inexpensive electricity, and would not use fossil fuels.

7. List disadvantages of the Bay of Fundy power plant. **Turbines could destroy fish. Tides on the**
   Atlantic coast could be affected, resulting in flooded lowlands, destruction of salt marshes and
   habitats, and contamination of wells.

8. Explain how the Bay of Fundy power plant could bring more jobs while destroying others.
   At high tide, some farmlands and towns could be flooded. At low tide, some Boston harbor
   channels might become too shallow to use.

STUDY GUIDE

● Ocean Waves and Tides

Match the items in Column I with the terms in Column II. Write the letter on the blank at the left.

Column I

d 1. Force exerted by objects on every other object

j 2. Exerts a strong pull on water in the ocean

j 3. Movement in which water, whether in an ocean, lake, or swimming
   pool, alternately rises and falls

f 4. Difference between high and low tide

a 5. Created by the collapse of a wave

c 6. Highest point of a wave

g 7. A rise and fall in the surface level of the ocean caused by a giant wave

e 8. When high tides are higher and low tides are lower than normal

k 9. Vertical distance between a wave's crest and trough

l 10. Horizontal distance between crests of successive waves

h 11. Lowest point of a wave

b 12. When high tides are lower and low tides are higher than normal

Column II

a. breaker
b. neap tide
c. crest
d. gravity
e. spring tide
f. tidal range
g. tide
h. trough
i. moon
j. wave
k. wave height
l. wavelength

13. Label Figures 1–4 as either *spring tide* or *neap tide*.

FIGURE 1 FIGURE 2 FIGURE 3 FIGURE 4

spring tide spring tide neap tide neap tide

Chapter 18

Text Pages 510–518

STUDY GUIDE

● Life in the Ocean

Find the term for each clue in the puzzle and circle it. The terms may read across or down. Then write the term after the clue.

1. Group of ocean life that includes larger animals that swim **nekton**

2. Gas used in the process of photosynthesis **carbon dioxide**

3. Used with sunlight and carbon dioxide by plants in photosynthesis **nutrients**

4. Colony of corals **reef**

5. Needed in photosynthesis but not in chemosynthesis **sunlight**

6. Example of an animal plankton **jellyfish**

7. Process by which plants produce food and oxygen **photosynthesis**

8. Animal in the nekton group that roams the entire ocean **whale**

9. Benthos that creates a hard calcium outer covering **coral**

10. Food-chain process that takes place along the mid-ocean ridges and does not require sunlight **chemosynthesis**

11. Example of plant plankton **diatoms**

12. Group made up of drifting plants and animals **plankton**

13. Gas used in respiration and released in photosynthesis **oxygen**

14. Group made up of organisms that live on the ocean floor **benthos**

15. Example of nekton **turtles**

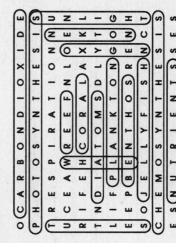

Chapter 18

Text Pages 504–509

STUDY GUIDE

● The Seafloor

Write the term that matches each description below on the spaces provided. Then complete Item 9.

1. S **E** A M O U N T

2. A B Y S S A L P **L** A I N

3. C **O** N T I N E N T A L S L O P E

4. P **L** A C E R D E P O S I T S

5. C O N T I N E N T A L S H E L **L** **F**

6. M A N G A N E **S** E

7. T **R** E N C H

8. M I D - **O** C E A N R I D G E S

1. Inactive volcano found on the ocean floor

2. Flat seafloor in the deep ocean formed when deposits of sediment filled valleys

3. Area at the end of the continental shelf

4. Sediments found where rivers meet oceans

5. Gently sloping part of the continent that extends underwater

6. Mineral concentrated with nickel and cobalt in nodules found across 20 to 50 percent of the Pacific basin

7. Deep ocean valley that forms where one part of the seafloor is pushed beneath another part

8. Underwater mountain chains that form when forces within Earth cause the seafloor to spread apart

9. Write the letters in the boxes on the lines provided. Then unscramble the letters to complete the sentence that follows.

E L O A F S R O

All of the features identified in this activity are part of the **seafloor** _____.

Chapter 18
STUDY GUIDE

Pollution and Marine Life

Use the terms in the box to complete the sentences in the following paragraphs.

soil sediments	solid wastes	industrial waste
plankton	oil spills	food chains
pollution	herbicides	organisms

When harmful waste products, chemicals, and substances get into an environment,

pollution _____ occurs. Humans can pollute the ocean in many ways. Most ocean

pollution is located along the coasts of the continents. Manufacturers may release

industrial waste _____ like chemicals and metals. People use pesticides, including

herbicides _____, that enter the ocean through runoff. People can carelessly dispose of

such **solid wastes** _____ as plastic bags and plastic beverage can rings. Leaks in offshore

oil wells or tanker collisions can lead to **oil spills** _____. Even

soil sediments _____ from plowed fields can pollute the ocean environment.

When an ocean becomes polluted, the effects are felt far beyond the water's limits. There is

disruption of **food chains** _____, and there can be severe effects on Earth's oxygen

supply, much of which is produced by **plankton** _____. All these forms of human

pollution can cause the death of many **organisms** _____ not only in the ocean but

throughout Earth.

For each type of pollution of the ocean identified, number the events that harm ocean organisms in the order that they happen.

A. Pollution by human sewage

5   Bacteria use up oxygen needed by other organisms and those organisms die.

2   The sewage fertilizes the water.

1   Human sewage flows into the ocean.

4   Bacteria decompose the plankton when they die.

3   Some plankton reproduce more quickly because of the fertilized water.

B. Pollution by soil runoff

4   The filter-feeding systems of oysters and clams become clogged.

1   Human activities tear up the soil.

3   Silt accumulates in coastal areas.

2   Rain washes the soil into streams and eventually into the ocean.

Chapter 19
STUDY GUIDE

Population Impact on the Environment

Cross out the statements that are NOT correct.

1. A population is the total number of individuals of a particular species in a particular area.

2. ~~Earth's population is decreasing.~~

3. *Population explosion* is a term that is used to describe the rapid rate at which people are reproducing.

4. Each day, more than 260 000 people are added to Earth's population.

5. In the 1800s, the world population reached about a billion.

6. ~~During the last two centuries, the rate of population increase has slowed.~~

7. ~~The number of people on Earth does not affect the environment.~~

8. ~~In the past, Earth didn't have resources to support the population.~~

9. ~~The average person in the United States uses less energy than the average person in the rest of the world.~~

10. Electricity is generated by burning fuels.

11. Plastic products affect the environment.

12. ~~Removing Earth's resources doesn't affect the land.~~

13. Shaping resources into usable products affects the environment.

14. ~~Farming prevents topsoil from being lost.~~

15. Much of the food you eat is grown using chemicals in the process.

16. The population is predicted to be 14 billion sometime in the next century.

17. Modern medicine, better sanitation, and better nutrition have all helped to slow the death rate.

Chapter 19
STUDY GUIDE
Using the Land

Determine whether each of the following statements is true or false. Write the word "true" or "false" in the blank. Then in the space below the statements, tell why each false statement is false.

false   1. Most of the land on Earth is farmland.

false   2. Since 1985, the problem of world hunger has been solved.

false   3. Eroded topsoil can be replaced within a year.

true   4. Herbicides and pesticides, often used on crops, may contaminate waterways.

true   5. Destruction of trees causes other plants and animals to die.

true   6. In a sanitary landfill, each day's deposit of garbage is covered with dirt.

true   7. Hazardous waste may be poisonous or radioactive.

true   8. Batteries and medicine are two kinds of hazardous waste.

true   9. Many cities put trash and garbage in landfills.

false   10. Paving the land is one way to protect the environment.

true   11. Conservation is a careful use of resources.

false   12. Conservation eliminates all damage to the environment.

true   13. Piling up cut grass and leaves so they can decompose is called composting.

1. Fifteen million out of 130 million square kilometers is farmland.

2. About 20 percent of the people in the world live in poverty and hunger.

3. Topsoil doesn't evolve quickly. It can take more than 1000 years for new topsoil to evolve and replace the eroded topsoil.

10. Asphalt and concrete absorb solar radiation. The atmosphere is then heated by conduction, and the air temperature rises. Less water is able to soak into the soil, reducing the amount of water that makes its way to underground aquifers.

12. Conservation reduces damage to the environment.

Chapter 19
STUDY GUIDE
Should Recycling Be Required?

Use the words in the box to fill in the blanks.

garbage	require	energy	trees
natural resources	60	cheaper	
recyclable	40	mass	

1. An object is **recyclable** _____ if it can be processed and used again.

2. If you recycle, you will reduce the trash you generate in your lifetime by **60** _____ percent.

3. Recycling saves landfill space, energy, and **natural** _____ resources.

4. If you don't recycle, you will generate trash equal to at least 600 times your **mass** _____.

5. In some places, **garbage** _____ is not collected if it contains items that should have been recycled.

6. One problem for recycling paper is that new paper is **cheaper** _____ than recycled paper.

7. Paper makes up about **40** _____ percent of the mass of our trash.

8. If you recycle paper, you help reduce the damage caused by cutting **trees** _____.

9. Recycling one aluminum can saves enough **energy** _____ to keep a TV running for three hours.

10. Many state and city governments promote recycling. Some of them **require** _____ recycling.

Answer the following questions on the lines provided.

11. How are trash-collection fees used in some places to promote recycling? **People who recycle pay lower trash-collection fees.**

12. What are some of the economic costs of recycling? **Money is needed for workers, trucks, and buildings.**

Chapter 20

STUDY GUIDE   ● **Air Pollution**

Match the items in Column I with the phrases in Column II. Write the letter of the correct phrase in the blank at the left.

Column I

e   1. acid rain
h   2. acid
j   3. base
a   4. carbon monoxide
f   5. 1990 Clean Air Act
d   6. mountains and valleys
c   7. natural sources of pollution
b   8. photochemical smog
i   9. pH scale
g   10. sulfurous smog

Column II

a. Colorless, odorless gas present in some smog
b. Occurs when nitrogen compounds react with sunlight
c. Volcanic eruptions, forest fires, and grass fires
d. Landforms that help smog form
e. Sulfur dioxide or nitrogen compounds combined with moisture in the air
f. Goals to clean up the air in the United States
g. Formed when fossil fuels are burned, releasing sulfur compounds, dust, and smoke particles where there is little wind
h. Type of solution with a low pH number
i. Measure of acidity in a solution
j. Type of solution with a high pH number

Finish the puzzle below. Then unscramble the letters in the boxes to complete Item 15.

11. smoke + fog = S M O G

12. nitrogen + oxygen = N I T R O G E N   C O M P O U N D

13. sulfur compounds + stagnant air = S U L F U R O U S   S M O G

14. pollutants + sunlight = P H O T O C H E M I C A L   S M O G

15. Goal of the 1990 Clean Air Act =
N O   M O R E   P O L L U T I O N

Chapter 20

STUDY GUIDE   ● **Acid Rain**

Use the words in the boxes to fill in the blanks.

acidic	factories	soil
basic	nitrogen gases	wind
cars	Midwest	sulfur

The amount of acid rain in an area depends on the number of **factories** and **cars** in the area. This is because they are the sources of **sulfur** and **nitrogen gases** that become acid rain.

Does acid rain fall where the pollution starts? It depends on the **wind**, which sometimes carries the pollution away.

When acid rain does fall, the damage it does depends partly on the kind of **soil** in the area. Some soils are already **acidic**, and plants that grow in them can't survive when more acid is added. Other soils are **basic**, and the damage is less when acid rain falls on these. As a rule, soils in the **Midwest** are basic and soils in the northeastern states are acidic.

sulfur	coal-burning	jobs
car exhaust	public transportation	car pooling
cost	scrubber	coal
nitric acid		

Acid rain is created when moisture in the air combines with nitrogen oxide to form **nitric acid**. Do you know what the main source of nitrogen oxide is? It comes from **car exhaust**. Two ways people can help to reduce nitric acid are by **carpooling** and using **public transportation**.

Another source of acid rain comes from **coal-burning** power plants that release **sulfur** into the air. Power plants can help this situation in two ways. They can wash the **coal**, and they can run the smoke through a **scrubber**.

Why don't people insist that power plants make their exhaust cleaner? Because the **cost** of electricity would increase and because many people could lose their **jobs**.

Chapter 21

STUDY GUIDE

Text Pages 584–590

● Radiation from Space

Decide if each statement is true or false. If false, change the italicized word or words to make the statement correct and write your answer in the blank at the left. If the statement is correct, write true in the blank.

space	1. Unlike mechanical waves, electromagnetic waves can travel through *matter*.
true	2. *Radiation* is energy that's transmitted from one place to another by electromagnetic waves.
reflecting	3. A *refracting* telescope uses mirrors to focus light from the object being viewed.
true	4. In a vacuum, the *speed of light* equals 300 000 km/s.
can pass	5. Unlike visible light, radio waves *can't pass* freely through Earth's atmosphere.
radio telescope	6. Today, *optical telescopes* the size of three football fields are being used.
true	7. The *Hubble Space Telescope* is an example of an optical telescope.
true	8. Sound waves are examples of *mechanical waves*.
radio waves	9. Radio telescopes are used to study *visible light waves.*
wavelenghts	10. Types of electromagnetic waves differ in their *speeds.*
true	11. Most optical telescopes used by professional astronomers are in *observatories.*
radio waves	12. For us to hear astronauts' voices from space, the sound waves must be converted into *gamma rays* and then converted back to sound waves.
the same	13. Different types of magnetic waves travel at *different* speeds.
true	14. Earth's *atmosphere* absorbs and distorts some of the energy we receive from space objects.
true	15. The arrangement of the types of radiant energy according to their wavelengths is called the *electromagnetic spectrum.*
true	16. Both reflecting and refracting telescopes are *optical* telescopes.
true	17. *Magnetic* waves travel at the speed of light.

82

Chapter 20

STUDY GUIDE

Text Pages 568–577

● Water Pollution

A word has been scrambled in each of the following statements. Unscramble the word and write it on the line provided.

bacteria	1. Tests of rivers, streams, and lakes show that some have been polluted by **beairact** from raw sewage.
illegal	2. Dumping raw sewage is an **agllile** act.
radioactive	3. Barrels of waste from nuclear power plants may leak materials that are **taciodivera.**
aquifers	4. Water running through mines carries pollutants to underground **quaierfs.**
wash	5. Water is polluted every time you **shaw.**
reduce	6. Sometimes countries work together to **drecue** pollution.
quality	7. In the 1970s, Canada and the United States made two water **lautiqy** agreements.
hazardous	8. **zhousdara** wastes poured directly onto the ground may move through the soil.
disposal	9. If you have a question about how to get rid of hazardous wastes, call your garbage **plaidoss** service for information.
energy	10. A way for individuals to reduce water pollution is to conserve **neegry.**

Complete the chart by listing each of the following sentences under the correct heading.

- The United States passed it in 1986.
- The United States passed it in 1987.
- It ensures that drinking water is safe.
- It gives money to states to build sewage plants.
- It gives money to states to build wastewater treatment facilities.
- It requires states to develop water quality standards for all streams.
- Some cities still do not meet its standards.

Safe Drinking Water Act	Clean Water Act
1. The United States passed it in 1986.	1. The United States passed it in 1987.
2. It ensures that drinking water is safe.	2. It gives money to states to build sewage plants.
3. Some cities still do not meet its standards.	3. It gives money to states to build wastewater treatment facilities.
	4. It requires states to develop water quality standards for all streams.

81

Chapter 21

STUDY GUIDE

Text Pages 591–593

Light Pollution

Each number in the code below represents a letter. Use the code to decode the message. After you've decoded the message, answer the question.

Code:
1	2	3	4	5	6	7	8	9	10	11	12	13	14	15	16	17	18	19	20	21	22	23	24	25	26
A	C	E	G	I	K	M	O	Q	S	U	W	Y	B	D	F	H	J	L	N	P	R	T	V	X	Z

23 17 3   10 23 3   8 16   23 17 3
 T H E   S T A   O F   T H E

20 5 4 17 23   10 6 13   2 1 20' 23   14 3
 N I G H T   S K Y   C A N' T   B E

10 3 3 20   16 22 8 7   17 3 22 3
 S E E N   F R O M   H E R E

23 17 3   14 22 5 4 17 23   2 5 23 13
 T H E   B R I G H T   C I T Y

19 5 4 17 23   10 1 22 3   18 11 10 23   23 8 8
 L I G H T   S A R E   J U S T   T O O

19 3 1 22 .
 N E A R .

23 17 3 13   2 1 11 10 3   1 4 19 8 12
 T H E Y   C A U S E   A G L O W

2 1 19 19 3 15   19 5 4 17 23   12 17 5 2 17
C A L L E D   L I G H T   W H I C H

21 8 19 19 11 23 5 8 20   16 8 22   12 17 5 2 17
 P O L L U T I O N   F O R   W H I C H

12 3   17 1 24 3   19 8 13   3 1 10 13
W E   H A V E   N O Y   E A S Y

10 8 19 11 23 5 8 19
 S O L U T I O N

Name two things that can be done to reduce light pollution. **Answers will vary but could include:** Use low-pressure sodium lights, put hoods on lights such as flood lights, and turn off unnecessary outdoor lighting.

Chapter 21

STUDY GUIDE

Text Pages 594–603

Artificial Satellites and Space Probes

Study the illustration. Identify A and B in the illustration and write the correct term in the space provided. Then under each spacecraft's name, write the number of each item below that describes it. If an item describes both, write the number under both names.

A. space probe

2 ____
6 ____
7 ____
8 ____

B. satellite

1 ____
3 ____
4 ____
5 ____
8 ____
9 ____

1. This is any object that revolves around another object.
2. *Voyager 1* and *Voyager 2* are examples of this.
3. John Glenn was the first citizen of the United States to orbit Earth in one of these.
4. The moon is an example of one of these.
5. *Sputnik 1* was the first spacecraft of this type.
6. This spacecraft travels far into the solar system, collecting and transmitting data to Earth.
7. The spacecraft *Galileo* is one of these.
8. These transmit information to Earth.
9. Its path is called an orbit.

Match the project in Column I with its description in Column II.

Column I	Column II
c 10. Project *Apollo*	a. First program in the race for space. Goals were to orbit an astronaut in a spacecraft around Earth and bring him down safely.
a 11. Project *Mercury*	b. Second program in the race for space. Goal was for one spacecraft to connect with another while in orbit.
b 12. Project *Gemini*	c. Third program in the race for space. Goal was for astronauts to land on the moon.

Chapter 21
STUDY GUIDE

The Space Shuttle and the Future

Read the following statements. If a statement is true of a space shuttle, write SH in the blank. If a statement is true of a space station, write ST. If the statement is true of both, write B in the blank.

B _____ 1. The United States has developed this type of spacecraft.

SH _____ 2. This is a reusable space transport.

SH _____ 3. Its solid-fuel booster engines are recovered after they are parachuted to Earth.

B _____ 4. This has orbited Earth.

ST _____ 5. Cosmonauts spent a record 365 days in one of these.

ST _____ 6. NASA plans on assembling a future one of these in orbit.

ST _____ 7. This provides living quarters for work and exercise for people living in space.

B _____ 8. Astronauts have conducted experiments in these.

SH _____ 9. This glides back to Earth and lands like an airplane.

ST _____ 10. NASA plans call for crews to remain on board this several months at a time.

SH _____ 11. This would be used in the future to send equipment and goods back and forth to people working in space.

SH _____ 12. Its mechanical arm can be used to launch, retrieve, and repair satellites.

ST _____ 13. The Soviets called theirs *Mir*.

ST _____ 14. We called ours *Skylab*.

SH _____ 15. The *Hubble Space Telescope* was launched by this in 1990.

ST _____ 16. A purpose of this is to serve as a repair site for satellites and other vehicles.

SH _____ 17. Its liquid-fuel tank is not recovered when it returns to Earth.

SH _____ 18. Astronauts can only spend a short time in space in one of these.

ST _____ 19. In one of these, American crews have spent up to 84 days collecting data about the effects of living in space.

B _____ 20. NASA has plans for the future use of this.

B _____ 21. Astronauts on this perform many duties.

ST _____ 22. Several nations will cooperate in working on a future project for this.

ST _____ 23. While in this, researchers will make products that will be returned to Earth.

85

Chapter 22
STUDY GUIDE

Planet Earth

Use the words in the box to fill in the blanks in the statements.

revolution	ellipse	seasons
sphere-shaped	sphere	center
24 hours	365 days	rotation
axis		

1. A round, three dimensional object is a **sphere** .

2. All points on a sphere's surface are the same distance from the **center** of the sphere.

3. Images from space probes and artificial satellites show that Earth is **sphere-shaped** .

4. The North and South Poles are located at the ends of Earth's **axis** , the imaginary line around which Earth spins.

5. The spinning of Earth on its axis that causes day and night is called **rotation** .

6. One complete rotation of Earth takes about **24 hours** .

7. Earth's yearly orbit around the sun is its **revolution** .

8. One complete revolution of Earth takes about **365 days** .

9. The path of Earth's orbit is in the shape of an elongated closed curve called an **ellipse** .

10. Earth's tilted axis causes **seasons** .

Answer the following questions on the lines provided.

11. What is inclined at an angle of 11.5° to Earth's rotational axis? **magnetic axis**

12. What is the sun directly over at the equinoxes? **the equator**

13. Which season begins in the northern hemisphere when the sun reaches its greatest distance south of the equator? **winter**

14. On what date does the southern hemisphere begin spring? **September 22, 23**

15. At the March equinox, what season begins in the northern hemisphere? **spring**

16. At the summer solstice in the northern hemisphere, at what point is the sun? **at its northernmost point—over the Tropic of Cancer**

86

Chapter 22

STUDY GUIDE ● Earth's Moon

Text Pages 623–631

In the blank at the left, write the term from the box that matches the description.

lunar eclipse	full moon	waning gibbous
new moon	maria	third quarter
waxing	waning	waning crescent
moon phases	waxing gibbous	

moon phases 1. Changing appearances of the moons as seen from Earth

third quarter 2. Phase of the moon when you see only half of the lighted side after a full moon

waning 3. Period when the amount of the lighted side that can be seen becomes increasingly smaller

waning gibbous 4. Phase that starts just after the full moon

waxing 5. Period after a new moon when more and more of the lighted side of the moon becomes visible

new moon 6. Phase when the lighted half of the moon is facing the sun and the dark side faces Earth

first quarter 7. Waxing phase of the moon when you can see half of the lighted side, or one-quarter, of the moon's surface

full moon 8. Phase of the moon when the half of the moon's surface facing Earth is lighted

waxing gibbous 9. Waxing period when more than one-quarter but less than half of the lighted side of the moon's surface can be seen

solar eclipse 10. Occurs when the moon moves directly between the sun and Earth and casts a shadow on part of Earth

lunar eclipse 11. Occurs when Earth's shadow falls on the moon

maria 12. Dark-colored, relatively flat regions of lava on the moon's surface

waning crescent 13. Occurs just before a new moon

Write an F next to the statements that are false.

F 14. The moon rotates on its axis once every 365 days.

___ 15. The moon completes one revolution around Earth every 27.3 days.

F 16. The large depressions on the moon that are caused by meteorites are called crescents.

F 17. One half of the moon is always lighted because it faces the sun.

F 18. At full moon, we see 100 percent of the moon.

Chapter 22

STUDY GUIDE ● Exploration of the Moon

Text Pages 632–633

Circle the word in parentheses that makes each statement correct.

1. *Clementine* orbited the moon for two (**months**/years).
2. *Clementine* took high-resolution (**photographs**/sonographs).
3. *Clementine* could detect something that was only (2/**200**) meters across.
4. The South Pole-Aitken Basin is the (**oldest**/youngest) identifiable impact feature on the moon.
5. Much of the South Pole-Aitken Basin is in (**shadow**/sunlight).
6. *Clementine* found out that the moon's crust (thickens/**thins**) under impact basins.
7. *Clementine* studied (stars/**moon rocks**) as part of its mission.
8. It was decided that *Clementine* was a (failure/**success**).

Put an X by the sentences that are true about moon exploration.

___ 9. *Clementine* collected data necessary for astronauts to walk on the moon.

X 10. *Clementine* tested new sensors for tracking cold objects in space.

X 11. An example of a cold object is a satellite.

___ 12. *Clementine* got its name from these sensors.

___ 13. *Clementine* studied the sun as well as the moon.

X 14. The South Pole-Aitken Basin is the largest depression found in the solar system.

X 15. *Clementine* photographed the South Pole-Aitken Basin.

X 16. Ice may be found in the South Pole-Aitken Basin.

___ 17. If water were found in the South Pole-Aitken Basin, a moon colony there would be in danger from floods.

___ 18. Any type of moon colony would probably be powered by energy from water.

X 19. *Clementine* discovered that the moon's crust on the side facing Earth is much thinner than the crust on the far side.

X 20. *Clementine's* map showed mascons, which are concentrations of mass.

X 21. *Clementine* found out information about minerals on the moon.

___ 22. Humans are scheduled to walk on the moon again in 1999.

STUDY GUIDE

● The Solar System

Write the term or phrase that matches each definition in the spaces provided. The letters in the boxes make a word that answers Question 10 below.

1. E L L I P T I C A L
2. C O P E R N I C U S
3. E A R T H
4. I N N E R
5. F U S I O N
6. S U N
7. O U T E R
8. S O L A R   S Y S T E M
9. H Y D R O G E N

1. Shape of the planets' orbits, discovered by Kepler
2. Polish astronomer who proposed a different model of the solar system
3. Placed at the center of the Greeks' model of solar system
4. Planets closest to the sun—Mercury, Venus, Earth, Mars
5. Process involved in the forming of the sun
6. Placed at the center of the Polish astronomer's model of the solar system
7. Planets farthest from the sun—Jupiter, Saturn, Uranus, Neptune, Pluto
8. Made up of the sun and all the objects that orbit it
9. Light element found in most of the outer planets
10. What is the study of the universe called?   A S T R O N O M Y

STUDY GUIDE

● The Inner Planets

In the blank at the left, write the letter of the term or phrase that correctly completes each statement.

b   1. Mars is the ——— planet outward from the sun.
    a. third   b. fourth

b   2. Because of similar size and mass, ——— is called Earth's twin.
    a. Mars   b. Venus

a   3. ——— has great extremes in temperature, –450°C during the day and –170°C at night.
    a. Mercury   b. Mars

b   4. Venus is the ——— planet outward from the sun.
    a. fourth   b. second

a   5. The ——— space probes made many discoveries about Mars.
    a. *Viking*   b. *Mariner*

b   6. The atmosphere of ——— is mostly carbon dioxide.
    a. Mercury   b. Venus

b   7. The largest volcano in the solar system is ——— on Mars.
    a. *Valles Marineras*   b. *Olympus Mons*

a   8. One astronomical unit (AU) is equal to the avenge distance between the sun and ———.
    a. Earth   b. Mercury

a   9. One astronomical until (AU) equals ———.
    a. 150 million km   b. 15 million km

b   10. Water exists as a solid, liquid, and gas on ———.
    a. Mercury   b. Earth

a   11. Polar ice caps are a visible feature of ———.
    a. Mars   b. Venus

b   12. Mars appears red because of ——— in its rocks.
    a. sulfuric acid   b. iron oxide

b   13. ——— is the third planet outward from the sun.
    a. Venus   b. Earth

a   14. ——— is the larger of Mars' two moons.
    a. Phobos   b. Deimos

a   15. The ——— space probe mapped the surface of Venus.
    a. *Magellan*   b. *Mariner*

Chapter 23

STUDY GUIDE

The Outer Planets

Decide if a statement is true or false. If false, change the italicized word or words to make the statement correct and write your answer in the blank. If the statement is correct, write "true" in the blank.

Jupiter's 1. Ganymede, the largest satellite in the solar system, is one of *Neptune's* 16 moons.

true 2. All of the outer planets except Pluto are large and *gaseous*.

Uranus 3. *Neptune* is the only planet that rotates on an axis parallel to its orbit.

Titan 4. The largest of Saturn's moons, *Charon*, is larger than Mercury.

true 5. *Io* is volcanically active because of Jupiter's gravitational force.

Jupiter 6. *Saturn* is the largest planet and the fifth planet outward from the sun.

Voyager 7. Much of the information about the outer planets was discovered by the *Viking* space probes.

true 8. Unlike the other outer planets, *Pluto* has a solid, rocky surface.

seventh 9. Uranus is the *sixth* planet outward from the sun.

Great Red Spot 10. A large swirling storm on Jupiter is called the *Titan*.

farthest from 11. Pluto is not always *closest to* the sun because its orbit crosses Neptune's orbit.

true 12. *Charon* and Pluto are sometimes called a double planet.

true 13. *Saturn* is known for its rings and its very low density.

methane 14. The blue-green color of Uranus and Neptune is caused by *carbon dioxide* in their atmospheres.

true 15. *Neptune* is usually the eighth planet outward from the sun.

Chapter 23

STUDY GUIDE

Mission to Mars

Determine whether each of the following statements is true or false. Write the word "true" or "false" in the blank. If the statement is false, rewrite it so that it's true.

false 1. Only humans can carry out scientific experiments on Mars. **Robots might also carry out scientific experiments on Mars.**

true 2. The near zero gravity in space can cause human bones to lose calcium, weaken, and break more easily.

false 3. Human muscles are not affected by the lack of gravity in space. **Human muscles are weakened by the lack of gravity in space.**

false 4. It would take about three months to get to Mars and back. **It would take about three years to get to Mars and back.**

true 5. A robot's hands can be controlled by sensors connected to data gloves worn by a human operator.

true 6. A robot "sees" with tiny video cameras.

false 7. Radio signals travel from Earth to Mars in a few seconds. **Radio signals travel from Earth to Mars in 20 minutes.**

false 8. Scientists have already developed robots with sufficient artificial intelligence to work on Mars. **Scientists haven't yet developed robots with sufficient artificial intelligence to work on Mars.**

true 9. Because of the long flight to Mars, humans would face more danger than they do on current missions.

true 10. Body fluids move upward because there's no gravity to pull them down.

Chapter 23

STUDY GUIDE

● Other Objects in the Solar System

Text Pages 662–669

Solve the crossword puzzle by using the definitions provided as clues.

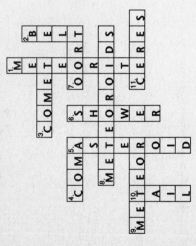

Across

3. Composed of dust, rock particles, and frozen water and gases
4. Cloud of vaporized gases around a comet's nucleus
7. Name of cloud that contains many comets outside of the solar system
8. Small pieces of rock from broken-up comets moving through space
9. Meteoroid that burns up in Earth's atmosphere
11. Largest asteroid in the asteroid belt

Down

1. Meteoroid that strikes Earth
2. Area between Mars and Jupiter where many asteroids are located
5. Piece of rock similar to material that formed into planets
6. Group of meteors
10. Part of comet that always points away from the sun

Chapter 24

STUDY GUIDE

● Stars

Text Pages 672–678

Decide if each statement below is true or false. If false, change the italicized word or words to make the statement correct and write your answer in the blank at the left. If the statement is correct, write "true" in the blank.

true	1. A group of stars that form a pattern is called a *constellation*.
apparent magnitude	2. The amount of light that Earth receives from a star is called the star's *absolute magnitude*.
light-years	3. The distances of stars from Earth are measured in *parallaxes*.
true	4. Very hot stars are a *blue-white* color.
absolute magnitude	5. The *apparent magnitude* of a star is the amount of light it actually gives off.
true	6. Another name for the North Star is *Polaris*.
greater than	7. The absolute magnitude of Rigel is *less than* that of Sirius.
true	8. The apparent shift in an object when viewed from two different positions is called *parallax*.
true	9. The pattern of dark lines recorded by a spectrograph can be used to identify the *elements* that are in a star's atmosphere.
true	10. The stars appear to change positions in the sky throughout the year because *Earth revolves around the sun*.
distance	11. A light-year is the *speed* that light travels in one year.
true	12. The apparent magnitude of stars is *greater* when they are closer to Earth.
true	13. Constellations that circle Polaris and are visible year-round are called *circumpolar* constellations.
Polaris	14. The star *Betelgeuse* is almost directly over Earth's north pole.
true	15. All of the constellations appear to be moving because *Earth* is moving.

Chapter 24

STUDY GUIDE

● The Sun

Identify the sun's features in the illustration by writing the name of each feature in the appropriate space below. The features are listed in the box.

core	corona	solar wind	chromosphere
photosphere	solar flares	prominence	sunspot

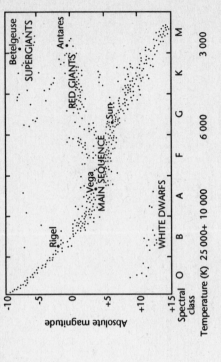

1. **photosphere** _____

2. **chromosphere** _____

3. **sunspot** _____

4. **core** _____

5. **prominence** _____

6. **solar wind** _____

7. **corona** _____

8. **solar flares** _____

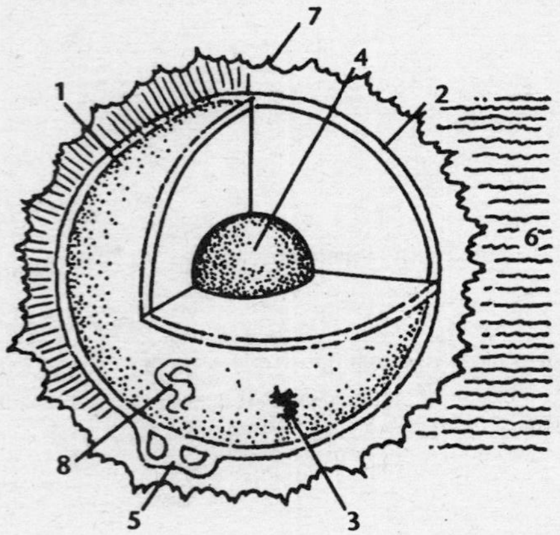

In the space provided, fill in the missing term. Choose terms from the box above.

core _____ 1. In the _____, hydrogen is fused into helium.

sunspot _____ 2. A _____ is a dark area of the sun that is cooler than the surrounding area.

photosphere _____ 3. The _____ is the lowest layer of the sun's atmosphere from which light is given off.

solar wind _____ 4. _____ is made up of charged particles that continually escape from the corona and move through space

corona _____ 5. The _____ is the largest layer of the sun's atmosphere.

chromosphere _____ 6. The _____ extends upward about 10 000 km.

prominence _____ 7. A huge, arching column of gas is a _____ .

solar flares _____ 8. Gases near a sunspot that suddenly brighten, shooting gas outward at high speed, are called _____ .

Chapter 24

STUDY GUIDE

● Evolution of Stars

Use the diagram to help you complete the following statements by circling the most appropriate term in the parentheses.

Diagram: Absolute magnitude (vertical axis, from −10 at top to +15 at bottom, marked −5, 0, +5, +10); Temperature (K) horizontal axis: 25 000+, 10 000, 6 000, 3 000; Spectral class O B A F G K M. Labels: Rigel, Vega, Sun, MAIN SEQUENCE, WHITE DWARFS, RED GIANTS, SUPERGIANTS, Betelgeuse, Antares.

1. White dwarfs are very hot stars that have (high,(low)) absolute magnitudes.

2. Main sequence stars are stars that fit into a ((diagonal), vertical) band that run from the upper left to the lower right on the diagram.

3. Although its temperature is greater, our sun has lower absolute magnitude than that of ((Betelgeuse), Vega).

4. On the diagram, our sun is identified as having an absolute magnitude of about (−5,(+5)).

5. Supergiants are stars with relatively (high,(low)) temperatures and high absolute magnitudes.

6. Red giants (are,(are not)) main sequence stars.

7. The absolute magnitude of Rigel is ((higher), lower) than that of the sun.

8. The temperature of Rigel is ((higher), lower) than that of the sun.

9. Betelgeuse is (hotter,(colder)) than Rigel.

10. Betelgeuse has an absolute magnitude that is ((greater), less) than that of Rigel.

11. A star that lies outside the main sequence is (Rigel,(Antares)).

12. White dwarfs and red giants lie ((outside), inside) the main sequence.

Chapter 24

STUDY GUIDE

● Galaxies and the Expanding Universe

Text Pages 691–697

Write the term that matches each description in the spaces provided. Place one letter in each space. One letter has been given for each answer.

1. M I L K Y W A Y
2. U N I V E R S E
3. L O C A L G R O U P
4. B I G B A N G T H E O R Y
5. E L L I P T I C A L G A L A X I E S
6. I R R E G U L A R S
7. S P I R A L S
8. D O P P L E R S H I F T

1. This is the name of the galaxy in which you live.

2. Scientists determined this was expanding by using the spectrograph.

3. This cluster of galaxies is made up of about twenty-five galaxies including the Milky Way.

4. According to this theory, billions of years ago the universe began expanding out of an enormous explosion.

5. This class of galaxies includes football-shaped galaxies.

6. These galaxies are usually small and have many different shapes.

7. These galaxies have arms winding outward from inner regions.

8. This is the change of color on the spectrograph as objects move toward or away from other objects.

Write the clue letters that were given in the answers: A S G A X E I L

Rearrange the letters to form a word for the groups of stars, dust, and gas held together by gravity.
galaxies

Chapter 24

STUDY GUIDE

● The Search for Extraterrestrial Life

Text Pages 698–703

Match the description in Column I with the correct terms in Column II. Write the letter of the correct terms in the space provided.

Column I

d ___ 1. Program that searches for extraterrestrial life

c ___ 2. Showed no evidence of the kind of molecules that seem necessary for life

b ___ 3. Life that exists beyond Earth

a ___ 4. A satellite of Neptune that contains molecules that resemble those from which life on Earth probably evolved

g ___ 5. A moon of Jupiter that may possibly receive sunlight on its ocean

e ___ 6. Sterilized so it wouldn't contaminate soil on Mars

h ___ 7. Sent a probe into Jupiter's clouds

f ___ 8. Molecules from which life evolved

Column II

a. Triton
b. extraterrestrial life
c. Martian soil
d. SETI
e. *Viking*
f. organic molecules
g. Europa
h. *Galileo*

Unscramble the following words to reveal what SETI stands for.

eth ___ the ___

chears ___ search ___

orf ___ for ___

xtttrrrreeeaails ___ extraterrestrial ___

elligtennice ___ intelligence ___